Down's Syndrome

Down's Syndrome

The Biography

Chris Nancollas

First published in 2012 by
Darton, Longman and Todd Ltd
1 Spencer Court
140 – 142 Wandsworth High Street
London SW18 4JJ

ISBN 978-0-232-52880-0

A catalogue record for this book is available from the British Library

Phototypeset by Kerrypress Ltd, Luton, Bedfordshire.

Printed and bound by Bell & Bain, Glasgow

Contents

Acknowledgements		vii
1	Langdon Down	1
2	The Rise of the Asylum	16
3	Prehistory to the Twentieth Century	34
4	The Twentieth Century	60
5	The New Enlightenment	78
6	A Day in the Life	96
7	The Twenty-First Century and Beyond	113
Bibliography		134
Index		139

Acknowledgements

This book would not have been written without the advice and support of many people, but two in particular stand out. The original idea for a biography of Down's syndrome came from Will Parkes, commissioning editor at Darton, Longman and Todd, who also drew up the outline for the book's content. Will has been a constant support throughout the process. The idea was 'pitched' to me (I think that is the term) by my old friend Brendan Walsh, the former editorial director of DLT, over a working breakfast at Paddington station. I had always told myself that one day I would be a published writer, and I am deeply grateful to the two of them for giving me this opportunity.

I am very grateful to the staff and pupils at the Heart of the Forest special school, who allowed me to see the teaching of children with learning difficulties at first hand. Particular thanks are due to Melissa Bradshaw, who acted as my guide and principal source of information.

I am equally indebted to the Forest of Dean Community Learning Disability Team for bringing me up to date with their work. The team comprised Terry White, Occupational Therapist, Julie Ann Gwilliam, Specialist LD Nurse, and Ruth Proctor, Speech and Language Therapist. Thanks are also due to Dr Paul Winterbottom, Consultant Psychiatrist, for his advice about current treatments for Down's syndrome.

My old friends and colleagues Alison Melton, Bob Swannack, Jeff and Sally Longley, and Tom Cullen were of great help in putting my thoughts in context. Chris and Alice Draisey also helped with information. David and Ann Adams also read part of the manuscript, and their advice about the prose style was very useful. Special thanks are due also to the Walsh family, of Ballintemple, Cork, for their encouragement over the years.

Finally, the book is dedicated to my wife, Sue, and my children, Tom, Sarah and Robert, who have had to put up with me over the years. It is bad enough sharing a house with a doctor, let alone a budding author, and they have been very understanding, especially given my frequent lapses into moodiness and distraction. I hope this goes some way towards repaying the debt.

1

Langdon Down

The story of Down's syndrome begins in the unlikely setting of the small Cornish town of Torpoint. This ancient ferry port sits across the estuary of the River Tamar from the city of Plymouth, one of England's most famous ports, where Drake played bowls before defeating the Spanish Armada, and the Pilgrim Fathers set sail for America. Torpoint was once a thriving centre of Cornwall's trade with Plymouth and a typical maritime town, full of commerce and grog shops and wild living, the first port of call for Nelson's press gangs. Then, in 1961, the Tamar Bridge was constructed, and Torpoint became a backwater, nestling unnoticed in the lee of the Rame peninsula.

Small forgotten Cornish towns do not generally have many internationally famous sons, but Torpoint has two. The first is the sailor Pete Goss, who sailed through a hurricane to rescue a French sailor in the Vendée round-the-world race, and was awarded the *Légion d'Honneur* for his pains. The second is the physician John Langdon Down, the man who described the syndrome that bears his name.

John Langdon Haydon Down was born in Torpoint on 18 November 1828, the son of the local apothecary. He was educated across the water in Plymouth, and worked with his father as an apothecary from the age of 14. Down's intelligence and aptitude for science were apparent from an early age, and at 18 he went to London and became apprenticed to a barber surgeon,

Matthew Coleman, on the Whitechapel Road. Surgery in those days was a fairly rudimentary affair, and Down's duties comprised bleeding patients, pulling teeth and washing bottles. The work was so crude that barber surgeons were refused the title of physick, or doctor, having to do with plain 'Mister'. In an affectation of which the medical profession is justly proud, surgeons today are still referred to as 'Mr' rather than 'Dr'.

Down did not progress much further as a barber surgeon, but was pushed by his family to study for his pharmaceutical exams. He attended the Royal Pharmaceutical Society in Bloomsbury where Michael Faraday was one of the lecturers, teaching the young Down about the properties of gases. Although he was not sure about pharmacy as a career, Langdon Down proved to be an outstanding student, gaining the Gold Medal for organic chemistry. He qualified in 1848, but did not register as a pharmacist. His mind was elsewhere.

His family, however, needed a pharmacist, and Down was pressurised to return to Torpoint. Although his elder brother had studied pharmacy, he had not qualified, and the rules had changed to demand the presence of a qualified pharmacist in the shop. He may also have returned because he was unwell, possibly with TB, and needed a place to convalesce. He resumed work in his father's shop, which was now being run by his elder brother Richard, and it seems that this was not a happy arrangement. The shop was badly run – Joseph Down, the father, had faced bankruptcy three times – and Down lacked the skills and the enthusiasm to be a successful businessman. In addition to being a pharmacy the shop was also a grocer's, tea merchant, coffee grinder and draper's, and Langdon Down wanted more from life than a striped apron and the daily grind of high street retailing.

His father died in 1853, and Langdon Down felt free to leave and follow his own goals, deciding to become a doctor. He entered the London Hospital in Whitechapel that year, and quickly gained a reputation as an exceptional student, winning the Gold Medals for surgery, midwifery and medicine, and the London Hospital medal for the outstanding student of the year. Twice now he had entered London colleges and excelled, and all this from a relatively humble background. He qualified as a physician in 1856.

He had become a doctor at an exciting time for medicine. The previous hundred years, the Age of Enlightenment, had seen the treatment of illness move from a haphazard mix of folklore and superstition to a discipline firmly grounded in scientific principles. The second half of the nineteenth century saw this process accelerate, and in this short period of fifty years the practice of medicine was revolutionised.

In 1846, William Morton, of Massachusetts, used ether as a general anaesthetic for the first time. The next year, in Britain, James Simpson administered chloroform to relieve the pain of childbirth. The use of general anaesthesia transformed the practice of surgery and obstetrics, making it possible to perform lengthy, more complex operations.

Smallpox vaccination was made compulsory in 1853. A year later, John Snow, the doctor who had anaesthetised Queen Victoria for the birth of Prince Leopold, ended a cholera epidemic by dismantling the water pump at Broad Street in London. This demonstrated that diseases were carried in contaminated water, and inspired the programme of public works that led to the creation of separate water and sewage systems. This was arguably the single most important public health intervention of all time, and one only has to see how rapidly water-borne disease returns in natural disasters to realise how much we take it for granted. (The second most important was the establishment of regular refuse collections, and it is often forgotten that the water board and your local dustmen are as important for your health as your doctor.)

As well as public health, Koch, a German, and the French physician Pasteur were laying the foundations of bacteriology, identifying the organism which causes TB, among others. Lister used phenol as a disinfectant, and Pasteur suggested boiling surgical instruments to disinfect them. The Hungarian monk Gregor Mendel discovered the basics of genetics, Darwin wrote *On the Origin of Species*, Rontgen discovered X-rays, Marie Curie isolated radium, and vaccines against tetanus and diphtheria were developed. Finally, in 1900, Landsteiner identified blood groups, and Sigmund Freud published *The Interpretation of Dreams*. In fifty years, the basics of public health, anaesthetics, infectious diseases, genetics, aseptic surgery, complex surgery, clinical investigations and psychoanalysis had been established.

For a prize-winning student like Down, the world was full of opportunity. At the very least, he could expect a post on the staff of one of the great London teaching hospitals, where he would be in the centre of the exciting new world of European medicine. Fame, and possibly riches, beckoned.

Instead, Langdon Down did something which astonished his contemporaries. He turned his back on the teaching hospital, opting instead for the post of medical superintendent of the Earlswood Hospital for Idiots in Surrey. Although a relatively well-run asylum by the standards of the day, the 'idiots', who were mostly people with hereditary mental illness, were largely thought to be incapable of help, and certainly not worth the career of a promising young doctor. The modern equivalent today would be for the gold medal winning student to announce that she wanted to spend her life in a single residential care home.

Down, however, was a more complex personality than the average doctor. He had a strong and simple religious faith which reinforced his natural compassion. In 1879 he gave an account of his early life, and recounted a tale of how, aged 18, he was caught in a downpour and had to seek shelter in the nearest house. Here he was served tea by a girl with learning difficulties, whose kindness and simplicity made a profound impression on him. From then on, in his own words, he resolved 'to make the care of the disabled my life's work'.

The asylum movement had begun at the start of the nineteenth century, and by the time of Down had started to run out of steam as the fledgling psychiatrists struggled to treat both existing conditions and the increasing number of people who were diagnosed as mentally ill.

There had been an early attempt to classify mental illness into 'lunatics', people whose problems had begun after birth and whose conditions were often potentially curable, and 'idiots', like people with Down's syndrome, whose conditions were present at birth, and who remained permanently disabled. The focus of the rudimentary science of psychiatry was mainly on lunatics, with idiots largely disregarded. So, although Earlswood was a modern and, in some ways, pioneering establishment, idiots were idiots and Down had apparently committed his life to a hopeless cause.

This was not helped by the haphazard provision of care for the mentally ill in Britain. The British Isles in the nineteenth century were a long way behind the continent, especially Germany, in the provision of state-run facilities, a somewhat ironic situation when one considers the modern NHS. The care of the mentally ill was largely in the hands of for-profit private concerns or charities. Earlswood, for example, was a charitable foundation, sustained by wealthy patrons and public subscription.

If the public provision of care in Britain was lagging behind the continent, British medicine was pre-eminent in one respect, in the meticulous history-taking and examination of the individual patient. British doctors were trained to think empirically, and to make diagnoses only after gathering the available evidence.

Langdon Down applied these arts to the patients under his care at Earlswood. He observed and examined his patients with great care, and in 1866 recorded his findings in his famous paper 'Observations on an Ethnic Classification for Idiots'. The central thesis of this paper is explained in the following sentence: 'I have been able to find among the large number of idiots and imbeciles which may come under my observation that a considerable portion can be fairly referred to one of the great divisions of the human race rather than the class from which they have sprung.'

In other words, there was something about mental deficiency which caused its sufferers to mimic other, physically different, cultures. Down claimed to have recognised Caucasian, Ethiopian, Malay and Native American types, as well as the Mongolian type for which he is famous. And while this would seem to us an extraordinarily insensitive way to label mental illness, it is important to note that Down saw this not as a racist sentiment, as we may be tempted to regard it, but as 'some arguments in favour of human unity'.

This would be a quite radical thought in his time, but Down was a man of enlightened and controversial opinions. In an age dominated by the affairs of men, when women were thought to be second-class citizens, fit only to be housewives and mothers, he championed their cause. His wife helped him to run Earlswood, and later, when they had an establishment of their own, they did so as equal partners.

Apart from the status he accorded his wife, Down's most important contribution to gender politics was to refute the opinion, widely held at the time, that educating women caused them to have retarded children. Along with this would have been the belief that educating women generally was a waste of time, a view which survived well into the twentieth century. We get somewhat blasé about rights these days, with the equality agenda seen often as a rich source of comedy, but it wasn't so long ago that we were behaving like the Taleban. The modern world is so focused on the 'now' that sometimes we forget how far we've come.

Down presented his findings about the ethnic features of idiocy in a paper to the staff of the London Hospital, and it became a landmark treatise in the history of learning difficulties. I will quote the relevant section here, because it contains some remarkable observations, and some ideas that were revolutionary in their time. I have also left it in its original language, which means that the word 'idiot' instead of the more modern 'learning difficulties' is used throughout. There is also reference in the text to 'degeneracy', a fashionable theory of the time which held that illness was a sign of degeneracy in the family, and likely to become worse in succeeding generations.

> The great Mongolian family has numerous representatives, and it is to this division, I wish, in this paper, to call special attention. A very large number of congenital idiots are typical Mongols. So marked is this, that when placed side

to side, it is difficult to believe that the specimens compared are not children of the same parents. The number of idiots who arrange themselves around the Mongolian type are so great, and they present such a close relationship to one another in mental power, that I shall describe an idiot member of this racial division, selected from the large number that have fallen under my observation.

The hair is not black, as in the real Mongol, but of a brownish colour, straight and scanty. The face is flat and broad, and destitute of prominency. The cheeks are roundish, and extended laterally. The eyes are obliquely placed, and the internal canthi more than normally distant from one another. The palpebral fissure is very narrow. The forehead is wrinkled transversely from the constant assistance which the levatores palpebrum derive from the occipito-frontalis muscle in the opening of the eyes. The lips are large and thick with transverse fissures. The tongue is long, thick, and much roughened. The nose is small. The skin has a slight dirty yellow tinge, and is deficient in elasticity, giving the appearance of being too large for the body.

The boy's aspect is such that it is difficult to realize he is the child of Europeans, but so frequently are these characters presented, that there can be no doubt that these ethnic features are the result of degeneration.

The Mongolian type of idiocy occurs in more than ten per cent of the cases which are presented to me. They are always congenital idiots, and never result from accidents after uterine life. They are, for the most part, instances of degeneracy arising from tuberculosis in the parents. They are cases which very much repay judicious treatment. They require highly azotized food with a considerable amount of oleaginous. They have considerable powers of imitation, even bordering on being mimics. They are humorous, and a lively sense of the ridiculous often colours their mimicry. This faculty of imitation may be cultivated to a very great extent, and a practical direction given to the results obtained. They are usually able to speak; the speech is thick and indistinct, but may improve greatly by a well-directed scheme of tongue gymnastics. The co-ordinating faculty is abnormal, but not so defective that it cannot be greatly strengthened. By systematic training, considerable manipulative power may be obtained.

The circulation is feeble, and whatever advance is made intellectually in the summer, some amount of regression may be expected in the winter. Their mental and physical capabilities are, in fact, *directly* as the temperature.

The improvement which training effects in them is greatly in excess of what would be predicted if one did not know the characteristics of the type. The life expectancy, however, is far below the average, and the tendency is to the tuberculosis, which I believe to be the hereditary origin of the degeneracy.

Apart from the practical bearing of this attempt at an ethnic classification, considerable philosophical interest attaches to it. The tendency in the present day is to reject the opinion that the various races are merely varieties of the human family having a common origin, and to insist that climatic, or other influences, are insufficient to account for the different types of man. Here, however, we have examples of retrogression, or at all events, of departure from one type, and the assumption of the characteristics of another. If these great racial divisions are fixed and definite, how comes it that disease is able to break down the barrier, and to simulate so closely the features of the members of another division. I cannot but think that the observations which I have recorded, are indications that the differences in the races are not specific but variable.

These examples of the result of degeneracy of mankind, appear to me to furnish some arguments in favour of the unity of the species.

If we ignore for a minute Down's theories of racial integration, what we have here is a remarkably accurate description of the condition, plus recommendations for therapy which remain relevant to the present day. Down's syndrome sufferers are short in stature with rounded faces, slightly flattened noses, and full cheeks. They lack the sharp prominences of nose and cheek bones, making the face cherubic in appearance. The eyes are slanted upward with a marked fold of skin, the epicanthic fold, between the eyes and the nose, which gives the face its oriental appearance. The hair may be thin, and the skin rough and lax. The joints are hypermobile, and Down's syndrome sufferers are more likely to suffer from atlanto-axial subluxation, or dislocation of the neck, which means they have to be careful about sport and exercise.

More seriously, patients with Down's syndrome are prone to significant abnormalities in the vital organs. They are more likely to be born with, or acquire, hypothyroidism, a condition which causes intolerance of cold, slow mentation, and constipation. Langdon Down actually described this quite well in his paper when he referred to their intolerance of cold, although thyroid hormone, the cause of the problem, would not be isolated for another thirty years. They are more prone to heart abnormalities, with septal defects and the life-threatening Fallot's tetralogy (where the heart is plumbed up incorrectly) being the most common problems. The eyes are also affected, with long sight, short sightedness, squint, nystagmus (involuntary eye movement) and cataract having a higher incidence in the Down's syndrome patient. There are problems with the digestive system, including malformations of the duodenum, and a condition known as Hirshprung's disease, where sections of the gut don't contract normally. These lead to difficulty absorbing nutrients and constipation, something else which Langdon Down acknowledged in his reference to diet. In extreme cases the duodenum is blocked. Both the heart and abdominal abnormalities can lead to the rapid death of the infant with Down's syndrome. Finally, the shape of the head makes sufferers more prone to upper respiratory tract infections, and Down noted their tendency to contract TB. The most severely affected child with Down's syndrome will be born with a list of ailments it takes the rest of us a lifetime to acquire.

The syndrome does not protect them, either, from the ravages of normal life. A person with Down's syndrome will get the same range of illness as the rest of us, and will probably be more prone to simple infections. Dental hygiene is a major problem, with the concomitant risk, especially in the pre-antibiotic era, of developing rheumatic fever, a life-threatening illness for those with heart defects. And in modern times it has been recognised that people with Down's syndrome can suffer from quite profound depression, especially in a hostile or unsupportive environment.

But it is their degree of learning difficulties which is the main problem for Down's sufferers, and which present the greatest challenge to their carers. 'Learning difficulty' does not just mean the individual has problems mastering academic subjects – we would all qualify if that was the criteria – but difficulty acquiring the basic skills necessary for day-to-day living. Things we take for granted, like cooking, cleaning, shopping and managing a budget, are beyond the reach of some Down's syndrome sufferers, which means they require some help and supervision for the rest of their life. It is as if people with Down's syndrome are not fatally corrupted but just normal people who missed out on some vital maturation factor, some undiscovered biological veneer which makes the finished product. With a good deal of effort and training, by all concerned, some of this shortfall can be clawed back.

It's an awful load for the parents. One of the things about parenthood which nobody tells you is that what a child means, practically, is about a hundred extra tasks a day. Gone are the leisurely breakfasts and an hour with the paper, welcome endless multitasking and constant anxiety. And that's for normally abled children. Children with Down's syndrome take longer to mature and acquire the skills necessary for day-to-day living, which means that their parents or carers have to keep performing these duties for longer.

People get very spooked by learning difficulties, and tend to overcompensate by hailing parents and carers as 'saints'. Although many parents of children with Down's syndrome probably need saint-like qualities, organisational abilities and stamina are the two most necessary attributes, closely followed by patience and an even temper. The second most common delusion about children with Down's syndrome is that they compensate for their difficulties by radiating uncomplicated joy and happiness. Well they may – some of the time. The rest of the time they're sulky, thoughtful, preoccupied, prone to temper tantrums, rebellious and untidy. Typical kids, in fact.

This brings us to the main error in Langdon Down's paper. He implied that all patients with Down's syndrome were mentally disabled to the same degree, and we now know this to be untrue. Down's syndrome is a spectrum of disability ranging from minor physical and mental impairment to severe mental and physical disability. This means that each patient with Down's syndrome is a unique individual, sharing characteristics with other sufferers it is true, but still unique. I emphasise this point because many of us, myself included, will have been guilty of regarding people with Down's syndrome as all being in a box marked 'Down's syndrome', not individuals like ourselves. If you think about it, what flashes through your mind when you meet someone who is physically or mentally disabled? Panic, probably, unease certainly and maybe a smidgeon of distaste. So you take a deep breath and try and speak normally only to find, to your horror, that all you come out with is a stream of mawkish, patronising drivel. So you feel ashamed, and start looking for the exit, and go outside, take a deep breath and think 'thank God that's over'. It's the 'visiting the sick' syndrome, sit round the bed for five minutes and make your excuses and leave. But imagine what it is like to have Down's syndrome and be on the receiving end of these conversations *all day long*.

Anyone who spends time with people with Down's syndrome will tell you that they exhibit the full range of personalities and behaviours that you would find in any branch of society. They may

be united in sharing some characteristics, but are otherwise independent individuals. They are not a Down's syndrome boy or girl,
but a boy or girl with Down's syndrome, an important difference.

What Langdon Down did identify, correctly, was that the disabilities of Down's syndrome were not immutable, but could with
proper exercise and training be improved. A child with Down's
syndrome left unstimulated may have struggled to speak properly,
dress or feed, or attend to the basic needs of hygiene. Down
encouraged at Earlswood a programme of primitive speech
therapy –'tongue gymnastics', a phrase to conjure with – basic
physiotherapy exercises, diet, and education in the three Rs,
reading, writing and arithmetic, which produced encouraging
progress for some, if not all, of the learning difficulty patients
under his care.

An important part of Down's success in treating his patients lay
in the nature of Earlswood itself. In 1847 a Victorian philanthropist
named Anne Serena Plumbe became interested in the care of
'idiots', and, after discussing the project with two of the leading
authorities of the time, Dr John Connelly, of the Hanwell Asylum,
and the orphanage founder, the Revd Andrew Reed, determined
to create a purpose-built facility for patients with learning disabilities. Lord Palmerston, Baron Rothschild and Lord Astley were
officers of the charity. After a brief sojourn in Park House, Highgate,
it was decided that the 'Asylum for Idiots' needed more space, and
Earlswood was commissioned. The architect was John Jay, who had
rebuilt the Houses of Parliament, Queen Victoria was among the
first subscribers, and Prince Albert laid the foundation stone. That
is a pretty impressive cast list for any institution, and demonstrates
that when the Victorians did philanthropy, they did it in style.

Earlswood is a large house, set in its own grounds, near the town
of Redhill in Surrey. At the time of Down it was treating up to 500
patients. They were housed in dormitories of fifteen, and there was
roughly one member of staff for every seven patients. This is a
pretty good ratio for an establishment of this nature, and meant
that each patient was known individually, a very important aspect
of the therapeutic process. Outside there was a large workshop

where the patients studied trades such as carpentry, shoemaking, woodcarving, and textile manufacture, while the extensive grounds were used to teach the principles of gardening and horticulture. The aim was to educate the patients and equip them with skills which, if not adequate to ensure independent living, meant that they could enjoy a useful and productive life. One of the patients, John Henry Pullen, became famous as a woodcarver, exhibiting his work all over London. Earlswood demonstrated the essence of good asylum care – cleanliness, discipline, proper diet, training and activity. This was Victorian philanthropy at its best.

Langdon Down was the architect of this achievement. As the sole qualified member of staff he was psychiatrist, counsellor, social worker, administrator and employer rolled into one. His first task was to order the use of knives and forks at mealtimes. He banned the use of physical punishment, preferring instead to withhold approval, and try and instil the notion that the child was responsible for his or her behaviour. Children who fouled their beds were woken, and the linen changed. Bullying and abusive members of staff were dismissed. Finally, Down oversaw the creation of the recreational and workshop facilities that gave purpose to the lives of the inmates.

As Earlswood was a charitable trust, the patients were drawn from all walks of society, but, as is always the case, children of the better educated and wealthy tended to make up the majority of the residents. Workers in learning disability in the nineteenth century had realised that in order to effect an improvement in the patient's condition, they had to be admitted early, from the age of five onwards. Older children did less well, and as patients with Down's syndrome rarely survived past their twenties, the need to start work early was paramount. Many of the children spent their entire lives in the establishment. It is worth remembering that the average life expectancy of a Down's syndrome child at this time was about twenty. Apart from the diseases inherent in the condition, all institutions in the nineteenth century were breeding grounds for TB.

Down's pioneering work had earned Earlswood an international reputation. *The Lancet* held Earlswood up as a model for the care of patients with learning difficulties. Many of his methods and innovations are still in place today, and Earlswood survived as a centre for learning difficulties until 1997, when it was closed as part of the plans for Care in the Community. Down should have enjoyed a long and productive career there, but he fell out with the governors over the employment of his wife, and resigned in 1868. They moved on to open their own establishment, Normansfield, which was modelled on Earlswood. This also became internationally famous, and received a steady stream of visitors, many of which were expected to perform in Normansfield's theatre. Down was elected as a Fellow of the Royal College of Physicians in 1881. Earlswood remained as a charitable trust until 1958, when it was taken over by the NHS. Thousands of patients have had their lives improved by Earlswood, and the Langdon Down family can justly be proud of their forefather's achievements.

In one respect, however, the asylum system failed. Patients with learning difficulties and mental illness were now shut off from society, hidden away behind the walls of these stately homes and grand institutions. A gulf was opening up between 'normal' life and the mentally ill, which was accentuated by the increasing autonomy of homes like Earlswood. Mental illness and learning disability, which may have been tolerated in the pre-asylum era, suddenly became something to be hidden away. Two of the most famous inmates of Earlswood were the Bowes-Lyon sisters, nieces of the late Queen Mother, who were placed in Earlswood in 1941. They remained there unacknowledged by the Royal Family, and *Burke's Peerage* reported that they had died (this information reportedly coming from inside the Royal Household). Katherine Bowes-Lyon was still alive in 1997, when Earlswood was closed, although by then the attempt at a cover-up had been exposed. Mental illness had become something to be ashamed of, something to be hidden away, left behind as the rest of us progress to the sunlit uplands. This, remember, was only fifty years ago.

Things have changed now, and not before time. The 1960s saw a great reappraisal of psychiatry, and among the beneficial effects was a realisation that large numbers of patients who were incarcerated in asylums did not need to be there. This was helped by the fact that the asylum movement had gone through some very strange incarnations, and the worst had become little more than warehouses. Gradually patients with Down's syndrome were moved out into the community, into much more appropriate accommodation, where they prospered. Which begs the question, of course, why did it take so long to realise that asylums weren't working? To answer that question, we need to look at the history of the asylum movement itself.

2

The Rise of the Asylum

For those of us in the twenty-first century, living in a world of at least partial enlightenment, the word 'asylum' conjures up demons from humankind's not so glorious past. I doubt if there is one of us who can think of the word without associating it with something shameful. Over the years, from Bedlam, through the horrors of the twentieth century, and down to the film *One Flew Over the Cuckoo's Nest*, the asylum movement has had a uniformly bad press. None of us would wish to be admitted to one, and if we had a family member as an inmate we would do our best to keep it quiet.

But asylums started for a reason, actually a very honourable one, and to understand their genesis I would like you to try the following exercise. Sit in a room with two friends or members of your family. Get one to groan 'uurrggghhh' loudly every two minutes. Then get the other to repeat a meaningless phrase like 'I told him not to do it. I told him. I told him not to do it. I told him', over and over again. I want you to sit there, without moving, just listening, for half an hour, and notice what you feel.

Now I would like you to imagine that in one corner of the room there is a young man with a strange look in his eye turning a knife over and over again. The room is small and he keeps looking at you with this weird gaze. More importantly, you can feel he is dangerous, you sense that he is going to attack you without warning. But that is not all. In the other corner of the room is a woman, dressed in rags and filthy, who is smearing the walls with her own excrement. You are alone in this dirty, stinking room, unable to think because there is so much noise, and scared stiff because you are half expecting to get knifed at any minute. I bet that right now you are thinking that asylums are not such a bad idea after all.

I have used extreme examples to make the point, but you get the picture. It is not just our need to have an orderly, tidy life which makes us want to shut the mentally ill away, but a genuine horror of what they represent. And the knowledge that deep down, at some visceral level, the same demons could lurk in us.

Until the advent of modern pharmacology they would be typical of the psychiatric cases roaming untreated in the community. Not all the mentally ill are noisy, or sit there spouting gibberish, or are psychopaths, or dirty, but a good many are, making their care something of a marathon for their carers. Even people with Down's syndrome, who are not generally held to be 'mad' in the disruptive sense of the word, can have their moments. So, as you sit there, listening and watching, imagine what it is like to have that day in day out for years.

By the beginning of the nineteenth century, throughout the civilised world, there was a growing realisation that provision for the mentally ill was inadequate. Care was haphazard, and largely dependant on means. If you were wealthy enough, you could place your mentally ill relative in a private care home, usually somewhere in the country, nicely out of sight, and out of mind. Poorer people were the responsibility of the family or the parish, and were kept at home, often in conditions of extreme squalor. Others, however, may have been orphaned or abandoned, making them, in effect, outlaws, taking to the woods or disappearing into the cities, where criminals and the dispossessed roamed unchallenged. As society moved from the agrarian, rural economy of the Middle Ages to the industrial, urban one of the Victorian era, so the mentally ill and the indigent became an increasing problem.

Asylums had been present in the Middle Ages, in fifteenth-century Spain, and, notoriously at The Bethlem Royal Hospital, or Bedlam, in London. Although these were the first institutions to house the mentally ill, they were little more than secure lodgings for the strange and dispossessed.

Often the main purpose of these early asylums was the incarceration and forcible restraint of those considered a danger to themselves and others. Very often the insane got no further than the town gaol, where beatings and abuse were rife, conditions which were only ever going to exacerbate the illness.

The first physician to recognise the importance of segregating the mentally ill in specific institutions was William Battie of St Luke's Hospital, London, who thought madness could be cured by isolating the patient from the outside world, including friends and family. He ran two private asylums in London for that purpose, although his hospitals offered little apart from isolation. (I thought the term 'batty', meaning mad, might have come from him, but it turns out it comes from the rather twee 'bats in the belfry'. Shame.)

Battie's work was taken on by the Italian doctor, Chiarugi, who pioneered the concept of the 'therapeutic asylum', a hospital catering solely for the mentally ill, where the therapy focused on the morally correct way to treat patients. His work was amplified by the French physician Pinel, who was the first doctor to explore the possibility of cure by psychological treatment, by trying to get inside the mind of the patient. Both Chiarugi and Pinel attempted to end the practice of forcible restraint of patients.

Their ideas spread across Europe, and were taken up most energetically in Germany, where Johann Reil, the third great founder of psychiatry after Chiarugi and Pinel, was moved to declare : 'The physicians of France, Germany, and Britain are all stepping forward to improve the lot of the insane. The horrors of the prisons and the jails are over. A bold race of men dares take on this gigantic idea ... of wiping from the face of the earth this most demeaning of pestilences.'

These bold men included William Tuke in England, and Benjamin Rush in America, and from this time the idea of the therapeutic asylum spread across the civilised world. The idea seemed to arise spontaneously on both sides of the Atlantic, which is interesting because it meant that disparate communities were coming up with the same solution to the problem. The earliest public asylum, in Williamsburg, USA, opened in 1772, and the asylum culture in the USA developed very much along European lines.

In Europe, the motivating force behind the asylum movement was the German physicians, who became the pioneers of the early discipline of psychiatry. Germany at that time was a series of small, autonomous states, which had the power to create community facilities. Each state had its own university, and this, coupled with an interest in madness, enabled the states to forge ahead with the creation of specialist institutions for the mentally ill. Medicine everywhere is highly competitive but this was especially so in Germany, where the desire for national recognition led to a race to publish original work on all aspects of medicine and psychiatry. The advances made in that country were so numerous that the nineteenth century became known in medicine as 'the German century'.

So what were they like, these early asylums? The key to understanding their function lay in the belief of many of the early 'alienists', as the psychiatrists were called, that mentally ill patients could be cured by removing them from everyday life, putting them in quiet, clean surroundings, and providing a regime of therapies and discipline. The German physician Himroth listed the requirements of a good asylum in his *Textbook of Mental Hygiene* – food, drink, sleep, exercise, fresh air and a good diet. Many of the asylums were purpose built, and resembled not so much an institution as a stately home, with classical proportions and extensive grounds. Quiet was essential because Himroth believed, as did many alienists, that madness was the work of inflamed passion: 'The passions are like burning coals tossed into the dwelling of life, or serpents that spit poison into the veins, or vultures that knaw at the entrails. From the moment that someone is seized by a passion, order ceases to prevail in his life.'

The protection was freedom, but 'the world gives us no freedom, only God makes us free'. So the order of the day for this 'irritation of the nerves' in the early asylums was control, cleanliness, spirituality and discipline.

And it appeared to work. Patients did respond to kindness and consideration. One of the first asylums in Germany was in Sonnenstein, which boasted gardens, a billiard room and a music room, a soothing atmosphere in which to practise the rudiments of early psychiatry. Great pains were taken as well to find trustworthy staff who would not beat the patients.

Perhaps the best known of these early German asylums was Seigburg, run by an enlightened physician called Jacobi, who presided over a regime of personal care where every patient in the establishment was encouraged to feel part of an extended family. This communal spirit saw all the inmates and staff share in the highs and lows of each individual. Treatment was administered sympathetically, and without coercion.

One of the problems faced by the early alienists was that the treatments available to treat the insane were primitive by our standards. There were hardly any drugs. Patients could be sedated with laudanum or alcohol, but that was about it. The other main treatments were physical – baths, electricity, galvanism, bloodletting and purging. Bloodletting and baths were held to be particularly useful for the more excitable patients, while purging and galvanism stimulated the lethargic. Restraint, formerly the mainstay of treating the manic or psychotic, was only used as the last resort.

The main function of the asylum, however, was to use the isolation to work on and strengthen the patient's surviving reason. For example, Dr Jacobi treated Heinrich N, a burly farmer, who presented with psychosis. This had started at the age of 39 as intermittent attacks which lasted a few weeks then remitted, leaving him sane until his next attack. Jacobi treated him with the standard purges and bloodletting, but also spent a considerable amount of time talking to him and examining him, gaining his confidence. When Heinrich had another attack, smearing the walls with faeces and raging uncontrollably, Jacobi tried to talk him down. This was only partially successful and finally Jacobi had to threaten him with the straightjacket and isolation, whereupon Heinrich began to calm down. Eventually he agreed to behave, and in time was well on the road to recovery.

The psychotic episode had been dramatically cut short because Heinrich knew and respected Jacobi. If he had been at home, he would have been overpowered and chained up in the barn, given food but little else, and would have been left in his own filth until he returned to normality. The episode demonstrates the effectiveness of both isolation – in the outside world there would have been no chance of calming him down – and the importance of the personal relationship between physician and patient. Haslem, the medical superintendent of Bedlam, wrote that to gain the patient's confidence the physician needed 'a mildness of manner and expression, an attention to their narrative, and seeming acquiescence in its truth'. These values would still hold true today. In their desire to improve the physical surroundings of the patients, and their willingness to treat each patient as a respected individual, the early asylums began with the very best intentions.

What we have been describing here, of course, are seriously disturbed patients who are obviously not in full possession of their senses. But what of Down's syndrome? Although many Down's syndrome patients are not of average intelligence, they are not clearly deranged, like the manic, or a danger to others like the psychotic. So what were Down's syndrome patients doing in asylums in the first place?

There appear to be two reasons. First, Down's syndrome patients, like other mentally ill patients, required care in its broadest sense, which, by the Victorian era, was a burden for many families. Second, at the birth of the psychiatric movement there was only one simple diagnostic test – people either had normal mental functions or abnormal, or alien, mental functions. Down's syndrome was clearly not normal, so sufferers were lumped in with the rest, under the care of the alienists, who held out the promise of improvement.

It was Johann Reil who first separated the mentally ill into two groups, the 'curables', people with relapsing mental illness like psychosis, and the 'incurables', people with hereditary illness like Down's syndrome. He argued that they required different types of hospital, and wrote a series of rules for the care of the 'curables'. Here we see already the problem facing people with Down's syndrome. The interesting and exciting patients are the curables, the lunatics, those with psychosis, schizophrenia and melancholia. The 'idiots', those with Down's syndrome and their like, were already settling at the bottom of the pile, needing to be shut away for their own good, but hopeless in terms of cure, or even improvement. A relatively passive idiot, one who did not draw attention to themselves, was likely to be completely ignored in the busy mad houses of the early nineteenth century.

The other problem was the profusion of idiots in those days compared with modern times. The causes of idiocy were genetic (Down's and Kleinfelter's syndromes, neurofibromatosis, congenital hypothyroidism, Williams syndrome, Fragile X, Prader-Willi syndrome, and phenylketonuria), infective (rubella, syphilis), dietary (poor diet and alcoholism), and birth trauma (prolonged deliveries leading to hypoxia, and deformed pelvis due to rickets). Genetic causes would have been exacerbated by interbreeding, while infection and birth trauma would have been widespread. Vaccination, antibiotics, better diet and, most importantly, professional obstetric care, has probably eliminated about 70 per cent of these, apart from the genetic causes.

Most communities, except perhaps only the very small, would therefore have their own population of 'idiots', and the idea is so ingrained that the term 'village idiot' survives to the present day, especially among urban dwellers.

(The last time I heard it used was in about 2007. I was acting as a doctor at a rugby match, and we were entertaining a side from a moderate-sized city. There was the usual banter between the sides, most of it coming from one of their supporters, an absolutely huge African man who had clearly been educated in one of our finest public schools. I happened to make some particularly asinine remark and he asked, in his impeccably fruity tones, 'And who are you, the village idiot?', to which I replied, 'No, team doctor.')

Up to the industrial age, idiots were cared for in the community by their families, and if they couldn't cope then the parish had a statutory duty to provide care. This system had not changed much from the Middle Ages. However, in the nineteenth century, something did change. At the beginning of the century there were only a handful of patients confined to institutions in Britain, much less than one per thousand. By 1900, that had risen to four per thousand. London alone had sixteen giant asylums, the largest being Colney Hatch (known as the Nut Hatch) with 2,700 patients.

Nobody knows exactly why this happened. There was almost certainly a rise in the physical causes of madness, with syphilis and alcoholism being rife. The profusion of asylum-building all over the world would indicate that each society recognised that it had a problem with the mentally ill, and that their care in the community was substandard. The living conditions of people with mental illness could be squalid in the extreme, with the disturbed often being chained up and left to rot in their own filth. A Down's syndrome patient with undeveloped life skills may spend their short life dirty and hungry.

Another school of thought held that the values of the capitalist society encompassed intolerance of deviance, and preferred to lock the mentally ill away. Communities which had tolerated and accommodated mental illness now shunned it, and preferred to hide it away behind the walls of the new asylums. The industrialisation of the country, and the shift in population from the countryside to the cities, may have accelerated this process by breaking down the interconnectedness which is such a feature of rural life. There is a big difference from being 'so-and-so's boy, you know, the one who's a bit simple' to being an unknown idiot roaming the streets of the city.

There was also the rise of the Victorian family, with the stern paterfamilias presiding over his clean and well-behaved family. No room there for mad Aunt Gertie, dribbling away and flinging her porridge at the servants. My own theory, born of thirty years' experience in the NHS, is that it is always dangerous to create a new service, however well intentioned, because it creates a demand which had previously not existed. One of the many things doctors don't know is how some of their patients live, and for the poor family with one or more idiot children the asylum system must have looked like Nirvana.

The need to deal with the problem of the mentally ill led to the passing, in 1808, of an Act of Parliament for the creation of County Lunatic Asylums. A similar public provision was made in some states of the USA, with the hospitals at least partially funded by general taxation. The Victorian era also saw a boom in the construction of workhouses to house the poor and homeless. The aim of all these reforms, it must be remembered, was to improve the lot of the poor and mentally ill, and remove them from the streets and gaols into institutes better suited for their needs. Unfortunately, as the energy of the reforms ebbed away, so did the quality of care, and both asylums and workhouses became little more than prisons.

However, this was in the future. In France, in the middle of the century, a Dr Itard of the Bicêtre Hospital in Paris wrote a paper on the 'Moral Hygiene, Education, and Treatment of Idiots', a groundbreaking paper which argued for the development of specific regimes for patients with learning disabilities. This led, in England, to the creation of five specialist regional institutions for idiots, the Western, Eastern, Midland, Northern and Southern County Asylums, the southern one being better known as Earlswood. And so we come back to Down. The pioneering work of Itard had ignited interest in the care of idiots, and the progress made by patients in these institutions was encouraging. A report made by one shows what they achieved:

> For idiots of the lowest class – speechless, inexpressibly filthy, unfit to sit at meals with his family, cramming his food into his mouth with his hands, choking on it and vomiting it back on his plate, the institution's training regime taught him to walk, to eat with knife and fork, to leave off his filthy habits, to dress and undress himself

properly, not ripping his clothes off, perhaps to articulate a few words ... to make him fit to be in the same room with his family.

Efforts were also made to impart basic educational skills to the patients. These are the accounts of two patients from the Western Counties Asylum at Starcross, near Exeter:

> O.P., a boy of twelve when admitted, was very backward in all forms of learning and could not use a pencil ... by careful and continuous training he can now write fairly and do sums of long division.
> L.F. This girl came to us from a home for feeble minded girls and could neither read nor write. She can now read easy tales, and write so well that her friends are delighted with the letters she sends home. She has also, moreover, become quite a good housemaid.

Here, then, was proof that the 'feeble minded' could be educated, and therefore face a more hopeful future. For those of us who able bodied and (relatively) sound of mind this may seem like no big deal, but in the forgotten world of learning disabilities this is a giant leap. If you could train someone with learning difficulties, then they could find some useful role in life rather than being left to vegetate in isolation. Although much of the world was still closed off, there were plenty of jobs for those with basic skills, like housemaid or servant for girls, and farm work or simple labouring for boys. With much effort and intensive coaching, the forgotten people could achieve the Holy Grail of modern society – becoming economically productive.

It is impossible to know what the patients themselves thought of this, because, as someone once remarked, people with learning difficulties don't tend to write social histories. In fact, we would have to wait until the 1960s for the first book to be written by a person with Down's syndrome, *The Diary of a Mongol Youth*, by Nigel Hunt, of which more later. So although we have plenty of accounts of what it was like to look after people with learning difficulties, we have no records of what the patients thought themselves.

What we do know, though, is that the mentally ill were widely stigmatised. I may have given the impression that nineteenth-century Europe was full of selfless altruists, and it is true that great progress was made, but the attitude of the general public was still a problem. Lunatics were still exhibited at fairs and events. The public could pay a penny to go into The Bethlem and watch the antics of the mad, which would have included public sexual acts as well as the usual ravings and dribblings. In 1814 the hospital had 96,000 visits. The conditions in Bedlam were primitive, with patients chained up, filth everywhere, no windows, and the inmates at risk of starvation and assault. The noise from the inmates was incessant and 'hideous'. The warders frequently beat patients, who were regarded as subhuman. If Langdon Down represented the good side of the care of the mentally ill, then The Bethlem was the dark side, where human cruelty was given free rein. And, although we may regard the warders who beat the insane as subhuman themselves, I wonder how we would react in somewhere like The Bethlem, where the inmates are screaming abuse at you all day long and the place reeks of human filth? How many of us would crack? It was the desire to avoid this problem which made the likes of Battie, Pinel and Jacobi so enlightened.

The mentally ill were probably also figures of fun in their communities, subjected to insults and beaten when they fumbled a simple task. I bet that hardly had the term 'Mongolian' been used by Down before some slang version appeared on the street. Worse, the mentally ill were almost certainly used for unscrupulous ends by the criminal fraternity. Someone with Down's syndrome, for example, with a limited ability to distinguish right from wrong, would be easy prey for the manipulations of pickpockets or burglars (think of *Oliver Twist*). And although there is no doubt that many were well cared for in their own homes, there were many that were not, some even being turned loose to wander the streets. Even in the better homes, the demands of the industrial age meant that few parents had the time to educate their Down's syndrome child. A place like Earlswood, therefore, would offer a better life for most of the children with learning difficulties. Sending a child away could be an act of kindness. We have an almost wholly negative view of incarceration, but for many learning difficulty patients, especially from poor families, in the nineteenth century, institutionalisation was often the preferred option.

We have so far concentrated on the positive side of the fledgling psychiatric service. The second half of the nineteenth century, however, is a different story, as the search for the causes of madness gathered apace. Psychiatry was split between two schools: those who were searching for a physical cause for madness, the neurobiological school, and those who favoured personality and social reasons, the psychosocial school. In the middle of the century, the neurobiological school held sway, particularly on the continent. The insane who died were barely cold before their brains were being inspected by the asylum doctors, although very little actually came of it.

Paradoxically, it was the development of psychiatry as a science which led to one of its most controversial theories. Alienists documenting the family history of asylum inmates began noticing that some families had an extensive history of mental illness of one sort or another. These were not just the recognisable 'lunatics', like those with psychosis and schizophrenia, but alcoholics (a term coined in 1852), plus those with what we would term personality disorders. It was the French physician Benedict-August Morel who first systemised this into the theory of 'degeneration'. Broadly speaking, what this meant was that mental illness got passed down in families, becoming progressively worse with each generation. A degenerate family may begin with mild neurosis in one generation, which becomes melancholia in the next, social decline in the next, alcoholism in the next, culminating in frank insanity, and finally, imbecility. Once the process has begun it is irreversible.

We may find such views laughable, knowing, as we do, that it doesn't quite work like that. But for the psychiatrists of the mid-nineteenth century, it made sense. Despite the best efforts of all concerned, it had become apparent that asylums were not working. What had begun with high hopes for the eradication of a 'pestilence' had turned sour as the insane stubbornly refused to be cured, and asylums became choked up with the chronically mentally ill. Any scientist worth their salt, when faced with the failure of a theory, is going to look for a hidden variable, and degeneration fitted the bill.

The theory became so fashionable that Down even believed that Mongolism was a result of it, being caused by the degenerative effect of maternal TB. It was believed that by the third or fourth generation following infection the family would have passed through Mongolism to dementia and sterility.

One of the original observations of Morel, which sparked his research, was that patients in asylums 'looked funny'. They had a 'special cachet in their physiognomy', which would be true of the many Down's sufferers and the 'cretins', people with congenital hypothyroidism. The degenerate becomes 'not only incapable of forming part of the chain of transmission of progress in human society, he is the greatest obstacle to this progress through his contact with the healthy portion of society'. So, Morel's advice is, steer clear of the mad or strange looking, but don't worry because 'the span of their existence is limited as is that of all monstrosities'. (Always comforting to be reassured, isn't it? Nice man.) A disciple of Morel's, Valentin Magnan, went further:

> Degeneration is more than an individual disease, it is a social menace: it is important to combat it with a rigorous form of social hygiene. One must not forget that the degenerate is a dangerous individual against whom society could and should reserve the right to defend itself.

You see what is happening here? The compassion and nobility of the early alienist movement is withering as the profession struggles to effect change, to be replaced by something altogether different, the need to blame the sufferer for their problems. And note too the appearance of the phrase 'social hygiene'. What exactly does that mean? That we hide the mentally ill away behind the walls of the asylums, or does it mean something more radical? As we shall see when we get to the twentieth century, something more radical was indeed what some people had in mind.

But for now, it was enough to confine the degenerates and mentally ill to the asylums. The theory of degeneracy spread rapidly. In Brookwood Hospital in Surrey, the number of patients in 1872 suspected of having hereditary problems was 4 per cent. This had risen to 40 per cent by 1890, which just goes to show that medicine is subject to the whims of fashion just like anything else.

An early disciple of the degeneracy theory was the Viennese psychiatry professor Richard Krafft-Ebing, who became famous for applying Morel's doctrine to the subject of sexual relations. He contended that an early sign of degeneracy was an abnormal sexual appetite, both in terms of quantity and quality. Initially, it is fair to say, there was some truth in this, because inappropriate sexual activity may be a sign that the mind is deteriorating. Unfortunately, the good professor did not stop there, and, fuelled by his religious faith, produced a book called *Psychopathia Sexualis*, described by Professor Shorter as a 'schoolboy's masturbationary compendium', which listed all the various forms of perversion resulting from degeneracy. Basically, this was everything apart from procreational sex. So masturbation, nymphomania, fellatio, homosexuality, lesbianism, transvestism and cross-gender confusion were all the result of mental illness. As, bizarrely, was premature ejaculation, a condition that carries enough psychological trauma in the first place without the added burden of thinking that you're perverted.

Fun aside, this had serious consequences. The influence of Krafft-Ebing's work lasted well into the twentieth century. Homosexuality was classified as a mental illness in the American Psychiatry Association's *Diagnostic and Statistical Manual of Mental Diseases* until it was removed in 1973. The World Health Organisation followed suit in 1990. Homosexuality was illegal in Britain until 1967, and although things are better, homosexuals, especially those in the public eye, have remained fearful of exposure. Krafft-Ebing's world of 'perversions' still carries the aura of shame.

Fortunately, just like any fashionable theory, degeneracy as a major cause of psychiatric problems soon fell by the wayside. But it has left an echo. How many of us would recognise that there are 'bad families' in our communities? All of us, I expect. Who would want to live on a drug-ridden inner-city estate? And perhaps more importantly, if someone said, 'We'll remove all these problem kids from your child's school and put them somewhere else', how many of us would see that as a good thing? Much as we would like to think of ourselves as enlightened, when it comes down to practical matters we often think selfishly.

By the end of the nineteenth century, the asylum movement, and psychiatry in general, had become mired in overcrowding and confusion. Asylums were overflowing, and the original aims, to treat the mentally ill with kindness and understanding, and to stimulate and teach those with learning difficulties, were forgotten as staff tried to cope with the tidal wave of patients. The Victorian era saw a marked increase in legislation regarding all forms of institutional care, creating more non-productive work, a curse which has afflicted the medical profession ever since. Here is Karl Peliman, who had worked at Seigburg, writing in the middle of the century:

> One cannot begrudge it to an old asylum director if his thoughts travel back to the old, and in this respect, better days, as he sits at his desk and answers questionnaires whose purpose and sense are never quite clear to him ... at Seigburg we had all sorts of time ... to dedicate to the patients, something which is impossible today.

The fate of the asylums is an almost classic human fable, which we will see repeated throughout the story of Down's syndrome. A group of pioneers formulate a theory, and prosecute it with energy, until they realise their goal of building secure facilities for a particular group of patients. Initially, results are good as the early enthusiasts work on their charges. Then as the word spreads, these asylums become more popular, and the volume of patients increases. Some less scrupulous establishments open, requiring legislation. The asylums acquire too many patients to treat properly. The pioneers retire, subsequent staff may be less motivated, bureaucracy increases and, imperceptibly, standards start to slip. Slowly the 'therapeutic' nature of the asylum becomes forgotten, and they become little more than warehouses for the mentally ill. By 1900, this had become a worldwide phenomenon.

As for the discipline of psychiatry itself, it was still regarded as a Cinderella science, barely one up from fortune-telling and astrology. Although some progress had been made by separating 'curables' from 'incurables', and numerous theories like degeneracy had been mooted, diagnostic psychiatry was still in the dark ages.

Enter perhaps the most famous name in the history of psychiatry, Emil Kraepelin, the man who laid the template for modern psychiatric diagnosis. In 1899, in his *Compendium der Psychiatrie*, he listed the major psychiatric illnesses, which he classified into thirteen major groups, of which mental retardation was one. This book was so influential it became the basis for the *American Diagnostic and Statistical Manual of Mental Disorders*, first published in 1952.

Kraepelin changed the face of psychiatry in a revolutionary way. Previously, the emphasis had been on finding a biological or genetic classification for psychiatric disease. Kraepelin instead looked at the symptoms, classifying his patients according to the severity and constancy of their symptoms. The important thing about this was his ability to predict outcomes, and resulted in a major reclassification of psychosis into two branches – manic-depressive psychosis, in which the mood of the patient changes, and there is a potential for remission or even cure, and dementia praecox, or schizophrenia, where there was no affective, or mood component, and which probably wouldn't get better. At a stroke, all the various weird and wonderful diagnoses of the mentally ill were categorised, and treatment plans could be made on that basis. Hardly anybody knows his name, but Kraepelin is right up there with the greats – Curie, Pasteur, Harvey, Barnard, Freud ...

Great though Kraepelin's work was, it perhaps further established learning difficulties as the Cinderella of psychiatric disorders. The focus was soon to be even more on the wild diagnoses, the manic depressions and the psychoses. But that is in the future. At the moment, it is worth considering the position of Down's syndrome at the end of the nineteenth century.

At the beginning of the century, sufferers from Down's syndrome were part of a substantial minority in society, the idiots. They would have been cared for at home or in the community, the level of care probably reflecting the financial circumstances of the family or parish. Then, as the asylum movement began, people with Down's syndrome became candidates for institutional care, along with other idiots, and lunatics, although for learning difficulties no prospect of cure was entertained. By the middle of the century, pioneering work in France showed that idiots could be improved, by intensive teaching and training. Special asylums for learning difficulties patients were built, and pioneers like Down made great progress in helping the idiots to speak, manage themselves, and learn. Unfortunately, progress was not maintained as the asylums became overcrowded. Hovering in the background was the development of controversial theories like degeneracy, which, for a time, had been discredited.

All this was taking place against the background of the most profound change. Western Europe, and Britain in particular, was experiencing the Industrial Revolution, where manufacture replaced farming as the main means of employment. The population streamed into the new towns and cities to find work. Fortunes were made from factory ownership rather than land or trading, and a new moneyed class began to emerge. The gap between rich and poor began to widen, and somehow, in all this, society lost its tolerance of the mentally ill, which combined with the new philanthropy saw them being removed from society, and shut up behind the walls of the madhouses.

The twentieth century would see the lot of the deranged and simple deteriorate even further, and we will come to that shortly. But what of earlier times? How were the mentally ill, and in particular those with Down's syndrome, regarded throughout history? Has their lot been one of continuous abuse and discrimination, punctuated by uplifting philanthropy? The truth is we don't know, but there may have been times when Down's syndrome was regarded in an altogether different light.

3

Prehistory to the Twentieth Century

The Olmecs were a tribe of Native Americans who lived on the shores of the Gulf of Mexico, and whose culture thrived between the years 1500 to 300 BC. They were one of the earliest Native American civilisations, predating the more famous Aztecs and Incas. The Olmecs built temple complexes, pyramids and large altars, and it is believed they pioneered bloodletting and human sacrifice as religious ceremonies. The jaguar was venerated in Olmec culture as a god, and artwork shows them mating with women to produce sacred offspring. Aside from that, the Olmecs invented a ball game, played in purpose-built courts, which was possibly similar to lacrosse. The ball was made of rubber, which they made by extracting latex from the *castilla elastica* tree, and because of this they were known as the 'Rubber People'. So, apart from inspiring numerous dodgy films, where wild-eyed priests cut the heart out of screaming virgins, they also, indirectly, gave us football. (Thank you, Olmecs.) In what was a strange precursor of things to come, it was believed that the ball game was in some way linked with human sacrifice, a tradition the modern football hooligan seems determined to revive.

The Olmecs were also famous for their carved figures, which took the form of giant heads. These heads, of which seventeen survive, have provoked considerable scholarly debate, largely because they don't conform to our stereotype of typical Native Americans. We tend to think of them, especially those from the Northern and Central Americas, as lean and fit, with hawk faces and deep dark eyes. Further south, it is true, they may be shorter and more rounded, but still with a recognisable physiognomy, round-eyed, weather-beaten and thin-lipped.

The Olmec heads are quite different. They are rounded with prominent lips and a broad, flat nose, more African than Native American. The faces completely lack the sharp, deep-set features of the Aztec or Inca. One of the first questions raised by the unusual nature of these sculptures was the possibility that ancient races had travelled between continents, something previously thought to be impossible.

For our purpose, however, there is one especially fascinating feature of these stone heads. Some of them have Mongoloid features, with the typical sloping eyes and epicanthic fold of the East Asians. When allied to the thick lips and rounded faces of these heads, the resemblance to Down's syndrome is striking. Even more suggestive is a small figurine, which, although labelled as a baby, has the short arms and rounded torso typical of patients with Down's syndrome. And, from a slightly later date, there is a small terracotta jug in the shape of a head, which has the unmistakable features of a Down's syndrome child.

As the work required to make these objects in prehistoric times was considerable, could it be that people with Down's syndrome were venerated in Olmec culture, regarded as children of the Jaguar, messengers, sent by the gods? Maybe in ancient times, so far removed from our mechanised society, simplicity and physical disability were not disregarded but seen as a virtue, a sign of divine powers?

It is difficult to know because American prehistory is mysterious, and has left us some puzzling artefacts. The most unique are the Nazca lines, huge geometrical figures carved into a plateau in Peru. They are only fully intelligible from the air, and as they were fashioned in about AD 400 it begs the question – who were they for? Similarly, a Mayan carving from about the same time shows a man seated on what looks like some form of transport, pointing at the sky with flames emerging from underneath. The theorists have gone wild, notably the writer Erich von Däniken, who thought it was conclusive proof that the ancient Americans had contact with aliens.

We can speculate all we want but modern scientific investigation has rather poured cold water on the theory by revealing that the facial characteristics of the Olmec heads do exist among the Native Americans, including the epicanthic folds and slanted eyes. So it is probable that they are depicting their own people, or, at least, gods with their physiognomy. But the nagging question remains – did they view people with learning difficulties as deities?

What is certain is that they would have had children with Down's syndrome in their culture. Down's syndrome is one of our oldest genetic diseases, spread uniformly throughout all cultures and races, which indicates that it goes back to one of humankind's earliest ancestors. The prevalence is about one in seven hundred pregnancies – I was going to say births, but antenatal testing for Down's syndrome has resulted in the majority of affected foetuses in the Western world being terminated. There is no racial or environmental factor in Down's syndrome, which means that all races are affected equally, including those who already have some of the facial characteristics.

So, the Olmecs may have venerated Down's syndrome, and it seems that another great prehistoric culture, the ancient Egyptians, also viewed disabled people as special. A papyrus in the British Museum, *Instructions of Amenemope*, warns of the dangers of mocking the disabled, deaf and insane.

> 'Beware of robbing a wretch, or attacking a cripple.'
> 'Do not laugh at a blind man, nor tease a dwarf, nor cause hardship for the lame.'
> 'Don't tease a man who is in the hand of a God (i.e. ill or insane).'

Dwarves were particularly well regarded in ancient Egypt, and could achieve positions of considerable power. The dwarf Seneb became a high official in the Old Kingdom, and is recorded as having several thousand cattle and over twenty official titles. The Egyptian deity Bes, god of sexuality and fertility, was depicted as a dwarf.

If a civilisation goes to the trouble of writing instructions for the treatment of the disabled, and, better still, regards one particular disabled group as especially gifted, then you might think that all disabled groups will be well treated by that society. It is possible again that the disabled or mentally challenged were regarded as having special powers, or at least considered differently by the gods.

By the time we get to ancient Greece, however, things are changing. Although Athens allowed a special tax to pay for the care of the disabled, their treatment elsewhere was harsh. The Spartans left newborn children out on the roof at night to ensure only the fittest survived, and threw weak and disabled children down a gorge in the mountains. A disabled child was a sign that the gods were displeased with the mother, another useful human trick to justify the punishment of the different and disadvantaged.

Aristotle was the first intellectual to propose social cleansing to rid society of mental and physical misfits, and Plato, in what sounds like an uncanny reference to Down's syndrome, thought that pregnant women over the age of forty should have their pregnancies terminated. Plato also believed that the body reflected the soul, so if you were ugly and misshapen then your soul was too. For the average disabled person, their circle of friends among the great and good, therefore, was likely to be non-existent. We rightly revere the intellect of the ancient Greeks, but a veil has been drawn over the dark side of their culture. Those who live the life of the mind don't dwell overmuch on the hoi polloi, and they found the need to care for slaves who had been injured at work particularly irksome. As one senator remarked when observing a slave break his leg, 'There goes another child-minder.'

And the Greeks revered beauty, their buildings, art and philosophy all straining for the 'ideal'. The classical sculpture of ancient
Greece is about the perfection of form, and it seems there was no
room for the disabled in the cult of the body beautiful. By now it
seems the idea of the mentally or physically disabled having special
powers had been well and truly forgotten. They were cursed.

Enter perhaps the most famous figure in the history of Western
medicine, Hippocrates. He lived on the island of Kos at around 400
BC, and established the first medical school, and also possibly the
earliest purpose-built hospital, the Aesclepion, the ruins of which
you can still visit today.

Hippocrates is important for three reasons. First, he believed
that the body of medical knowledge could be gathered together
and taught, thus defining what would make a good doctor.
Second, he believed that physicians had a duty to apply professional standards in both their working and private life, and formu-
lated the Hippocratic Oath for that purpose. One of the
clauses was 'I shall not give a woman pessary to cause an abortion',
which is one of the most contentious issues in the story of Down's
syndrome. Third, and most importantly, he believed that disease
was not sent from the gods, but arose from imbalances in the vital
humours of the body, like phlegm and bile. He associated disease
with environment, listing the conditions that occurred in mountains, lowlands, marshlands and cities, and he believed that the
physical setting of a hospital was an important factor in effecting a
cure. The Aesclepion is situated on the slopes of a hill overlooking
the sea, the perfect setting for 'airs, waters, and places' to work
their healing magic. Hippocrates described the role of a doctor
thus:

> Declare the past, diagnose the present, foretell the future:
> practice these things. In diseases make a habit of two things
> – help, or at least do no harm. The art involves three things
> – disease, the diseased, and the doctor. The doctor is the
> servant of the art. The diseased must join with the doctor in
> combating the disease.

Just about as good a description of the art of medicine as there has ever been, I would suggest.

Hippocrates was generally concerned with the accurate description of signs and symptoms, and was the first to describe finger clubbing, an important sign of lung and heart disease. He poured scorn on the soothsayers and charlatans who laid the blame for everything at the feet of the gods, particularly epilepsy:

> If the patient imitate a goat, or roar, or suffer convulsions down the right side, they blame the mother of the Gods. If they utter a loud cry they like him to a horse and blame Poseidon. Should he pass excrement the surname Enodia is applied. If he foam at the mouth and kicks, Ares is to blame.

Hippocrates thought the varieties of epilepsy, 'the sacred disease', were caused by fluctuations in bile and phlegm, nothing more. The symptoms of Down's syndrome, likewise, would be caused by an excess of one or the other, maybe combined with the environment, both physical and inherited, which welcomed the newborn child.

Although Hippocrates had done his best to evict folklore and superstition from medicine, socially the disabled were still persecuted. By the time we get to ancient Rome, that persecution had become perverted into something worse, the mocking of the disabled for entertainment.

The Romans copied the Greeks in leaving the newborn disabled out to die, setting aside two places in the city for that purpose. The founder of the city, Romulus, apparently instructed his people, 'You shall not kill a child under three, unless they be disabled.' The life of most deprived people in Rome was likely to be short and miserable. And there would be plenty of them, too, the presence of disease and malnutrition and interbreeding being as prevalent in ancient Rome as anywhere else. In fact, as the lives of the emperors tell us, incest was seen as something of a social duty.

Like most western civilisations, the quality of life for the disabled depended on their social circumstances. Those born into wealthy families would be well looked after, while the poor were not, often gravitating to the margins of society. Disability was not necessarily a bar to the highest office – the consul Quintus Pedius struggled to speak ,while the Emperor Claudius probably suffered from cerebral palsy. But while exception would be made for the high born, the slaves and ordinary folk would have had to get along as best they could. Quite a few found work as smiths because Hephaestus, the god of metalwork, was lame.

There is no surviving record of attitudes to Down's syndrome in particular. What we do know is that the ancient Romans viewed the disabled as objects of entertainment. Quite a few noble houses kept hunchbacks and dwarves, who were required to cavort around for the entertainment of guests. Some, it is rumoured, were ordered to have sex in public, to titivate the jaded appetites of the aristocracy. It was also fashionable for a time for the Roman matrons to keep a disabled slave for 'romance'.

It is impossible to say, of course, if Down's syndrome sufferers were put through this indignity, but, knowing the Romans, you have to suspect the worst. It is hoped that they avoided the fate of the two hunchbacks who were ordered to dance in front of the Emperor Commodius smeared with mustard. One shudders to think what happened to them later.

Despite the perversions and humiliations, life in the Roman Empire was probably better for the disabled and mentally ill than elsewhere, largely because rich societies tend to have more of everything, especially food, shelter and medicine. So, although someone with Down's syndrome may have been marginalised, their standard of living was likely to be higher than the barbarians on the fringes of the civilised world.

The greatest physician of the Roman Empire, and arguably the best technical physician that ever lived, was the Greek doctor and philosopher Galen. He was highly educated, with a sharp enquiring mind, and in his lifetime he drew together all the various threads of medicine and created the first comprehensive medical compendium. His philosophy was based on Hippocrates' humoral theory, identifying four humours – phlegm, black bile, yellow bile and blood. This gave us the four temperaments – the phlegmatic, melancholic, choleric and sanguine. These four temperaments were linked to the elements, phlegm being water, black bile, earth, yellow bile, fire, and blood, air. So, an excess of yellow bile, fire, choler, leads to excitement and mania, while an excess of black bile, earth, melancholia, leads to depression and sadness. Somebody with Down's syndrome would probably be regarded as having an excess of black bile.

Galen was also keen on anatomy, was one of the pioneering early surgeons, and laid the foundations of a comprehensive philosophical explanation for disease. His writings, though, make little or no mention of psychiatry or disability. The reason, however, that he is important for our story is because of his influence on the dominant force in Dark Age and early mediaeval medicine – the Near East and the religion of Islam.

The early Islamic scholars took the work of Galen and built on it, constructing the largest body of medical knowledge in the world. The physical location of Arabia (now Saudi Arabia) and Persia (modern Iran and Iraq) meant that they were able to absorb knowledge from the Indian subcontinent as well as Europe. Surviving texts indicate that mediaeval Islam had explored most of the avenues that we think of as products of the European Enlightenment. They had produced a comprehensive list of surgical procedures, and practised aseptic surgery, using medicinal alcohol. It appears they may have pioneered a simple form of rag and bottle anaesthesia, soaking a sponge in opium and holding it over the patient's head. They had a comprehensive list of drugs, and opened the first pharmacies in Baghdad.

More importantly, however, they pioneered the modern hospital, where cleanliness was paramount. They were the first people to use women as nurses and encouraged women to train as doctors, something that would be forbidden in England until Victorian times. The hospitals also employed people from other faiths, Jews and Christians alike, and did not discriminate against

patients. The world's first psychiatric ward was opened in Baghdad, as was the earliest psychiatric hospital, although it is not clear
if they would contain Down's syndrome patients. One of the most
significant developments for Down's syndrome did, however,
originate in the Golden Age of Islam. Muhammed ibn Zakariya
Rasi, a Muslim scholar and doctor, is thought to have published the
first treatise solely devoted to child health and development, thus
creating the speciality of paediatrics.

Muhammad had said that 'for every disease Allah has sent a
cure'. The most influential work on mediaeval medicine was *The
Canon of Medicine*, written by the Persian doctor and philosopher
Ibn Sind, or Avicenna, as he was better known in the Western
world. It was published in the eleventh century AD and it covered
areas familiar to us today – anatomy, biology, bacteriology, immu-
nology, ophthalmology, psychiatry, paediatrics and obstetrics, to
name but a few. The basis of controlled trials and experimentation
were detailed, as were the rudiments of hygiene. The work was still
being used in medical schools as late as the seventeenth century, a
phenomenal achievement.

The Muslim attitude to disability is contained in a Hadith, or
saying of the Prophet, which states, 'You are given sustenance and
victory for the virtue of those who are weak among you.' In
modern times this means the building of special schools for the
disabled, and the drive to help them lead as normal a life as
possible. It is difficult to find any specific reference to the disabled
in ancient literature, but given the civilised nature of early Muslim
society, one presumes that they were well treated. The mediaeval
Arab world, although at war with the West over the future of
Jerusalem, was tolerant of other faiths, allowing Christian and
Jewish enclaves in its cities.

This is not, however, an apologia for Islam, or an attempt to
elevate it above the other religions, because at the time its medicine was flourishing, the Arab world was busy conquering Southern Europe, with all the blood and slaughter that entails.

Islam was not the only religion turning its attention to the plight
of the less well off. Judaism, an equally misunderstood religion, like

Islam, is sometimes viewed as weird and vaguely sinister by modern Western secular society, although it is nothing more than a highly complex series of laws defining the relationship between Jews and God, and Jews and the rest of the world. Within those laws are the need to protect the poor and unfortunate, and the Jew's duty to contribute to the welfare of others.

Similarly, Christianity had its origins in compassion and the need to 'love thy neighbour as thyself', although like many of Jesus' best sayings it is open to interpretation either way. But the central message is clear: 'Do unto others as you would have done to yourself.'

Each of the great monotheistic religions, therefore, has at its heart compassion and the need to help others less fortunate than oneself. From the birth of Christ through to the Enlightenment, this would be the guiding principle behind the treatment of the sick and disabled in society. The Arab world was building hospitals from the sixth century onwards, and the spread of Christianity, especially the establishment of monastic orders, placed learning and medical centres within reach of at least some of the population. Without them there would have been almost nothing, the barbarian tribes having to manage as best as they could with little knowledge or experience. Life expectancy for a monk in the early Middle Ages could be fifty plus, whereas most Celts of the Dark Ages were dead by forty.

This is not to deny that religion has been responsible for terrible things over the years, but it seems to me that we are in danger of remembering only the bad things about faith, and are distorting a common history that is part of our legacy. Mention the mediaeval Catholic Church to most people today and they will immediately think of Inquisitions, secret societies, burnings, flayings, sinister Popes and venal monks. And, yes, all these things are true, but there were also a lot of men and women devoting their lives to good works, the monasteries were centres of learning and medicine, and the local church was the centre of the village social and spiritual life. From the fall of Rome to the dissolution of the monasteries, the religious centres kept alive the feeble flame of learning and medicine.

But they also had a much more important effect. Even the most dissolute could not hide the central message of Christianity, the need to look after those less fortunate than ourselves. From mediaeval times until the creation of the modern welfare state this has been the driving factor behind the care of the disadvantaged. Without it I am sure that the lot of people with Down's syndrome would have been worse.

There is also a tendency in the modern world to look past the Middle Ages and invest old tribes like the Celts with some kind of ancient, forgotten spirituality, holding them up as moral beacons in a dark world. As a Celt myself, I think that is wishful thinking. We may revere oak trees and such, but I very much doubt if my ancestors would have been interested in much else apart from war and intoxication. Certainly, I fear that the disabled would have been ignored, and maybe mocked, just as they were in ancient Rome, if they weren't regarded as useless and slaughtered at birth. To be honest, I don't know, but I think we are in danger of using double standards to suit our prejudices.

So, what would have been the social position of the person with learning disability in the Middle Ages? If we take England after the Norman Conquest, the social structure starts at the top with the king, followed by the Norman nobles and followers. This 5 per cent of the population owned all the land. At the bottom of society there were slaves, about 10 per cent of the population, and in the middle, the vast majority of the rest, the villeins, cottars, boarders and the like, who rented land from the lords and paid tithes for rent. Most of these people were illiterate. The churches and monasteries held the only literate people, and for the average Englishman the church, the Catholic Church, was his main source of culture as well as spiritual nourishment. Only about 10 per cent of the population lived in urban centres, the rest being scattered throughout the countryside.

Life expectancy was short because of high infant mortality and disease. Aside from the range of usually fatal infectious diseases, the Middle Ages had several chronic diseases which caused disfigurement and eventual death, the two most notable being scrofula, the Kings Evil, and leprosy, the disfiguring skin disease. Scrofula, or tuberculous lymphadenopathy, caused the glands in the neck to become swollen and often erupted into weeping sores, the effect horrible to behold. Leprosy caused skin flaking and produced distorted features, again giving patients an appearance so hideous that people could not bear to see them. Both were known to be spread by contact, probably through breathing infected droplets, and both were treated with isolation. By 1300 there were over 19,000 leper hospitals in Europe. Of the two, it was probably better to have scrofula, or the Kings Evil, as it was known, because it was believed that it could be cured by the touch of a king.

Isolating sufferers with a particular set of symptoms will resonate in the future history of the asylums, and some philosophers, notably Michel Foucault, speculated that the decline of leprosy meant that society had to find something to take its place, choosing instead mental illness. Certainly the idea that people with learning difficulties are not welcome in mainstream society is one which resonates throughout the story of Down's syndrome.

There were other, less serious, infections and diseases that would affect appearance. Blindness was common due to trachoma, while skin infections and weeping sores caused by contact with animals would be ubiquitous. Other disabilities would be caused by birth trauma, congenital disease, and accidents or battle injuries. One of the most disfiguring illnesses was caused by neurofibromatosis, which can produce gross deformity of the skeleton. The Elephant Man, of film and book fame, possibly suffered from this.

Aside from physical deformities, there were almost certainly many more patients with mental retardation in the community. Antenatal infection with rubella, birth trauma and childhood infections like meningitis, as well as congenital disease such as Down's syndrome would mean a much higher percentage of people with learning disability in the general population.

Except, what does the term 'learning disability' mean, in the context of a rural agrarian, illiterate, peasant society? The reason I ask this question is because there is something which puzzles me about the whole Down's syndrome story. I have no doubt that the terracotta jug made by the ancient Mexicans depicts Down's syndrome, yet despite the fact that it has a recognisable set of clinical features, we have to wait until the sixteenth century before there is any depiction in European art – *The Adoration of the Magi* by an unknown Flemish artist – and the nineteenth before it is described clinically. For the best part of two thousand years Down's syndrome goes unrecognised. Why?

The answer, I think, is complex. It would not be for the lack of observation, because in those two thousand years there would have been plenty of intelligent, meticulous people capable of recognising a particular strand of humanity. This leaves us with two possibilities, the first being that there were many fewer people with Down's syndrome. This is not impossible, as the physical problems associated with the condition would lead to a high proportion of sufferers dying at birth or soon after. On the other hand, without modern antenatal screening and therapeutic abortion, one would presume that more people were born with Down's syndrome, so this doesn't quite fit. Perhaps women had children younger, so the age factor doesn't come into play, but even so there must have been plenty of people with Down's syndrome around.

The second thing that occurred to me was that Down's syndrome was not recognised because the sufferers did not particularly stand out. By modern standards Down's syndrome has an absolutely unique physical appearance, but in the Middle Ages, the features of Down's syndrome were probably unremarkable. Every village would have its share of the disabled, people with birth deformities, those with limbs withered by polio, cleft palate, missing eyes and ears, weeping eyes, hunchbacks and dwarfs. Those who were of normal anatomical proportions could be disfigured by scrofula, leprosy, eczema, psoriasis, scabs, boils, birthmarks, smallpox, skin tumours and injury. Mediaeval punishments included burning, flaying, amputation, blinding and maiming. Against such a litany of physical ailments, the clinical features of Down's syndrome are relatively mild, so much so that they would probably pass for normal.

Similarly, the degree of learning difficulty, which stands out in modern society, would be much less obvious in mediaeval society. Nearly everybody worked the land, with relatively primitive tools which were easily mastered. The work was hard and physical, but not intellectually demanding, and probably well within the capabilities of a moderately able person with Down's syndrome. And because there were, for reasons listed above, probably far more children and young adults with learning difficulties due to the presence of disease and birth trauma, I suspect the society had got used to dealing with it, and worked on making the sufferers as useful as possible.

So, in a society where sizeable numbers of children were subject to what we would call developmental delay, the child with Down's syndrome would not stand out as they would in the modern world. I wonder, too, if there was a more general tolerance of disability, especially in the early Middle Ages up to about the thirteenth century. Perhaps the relatively able Down's syndrome person was, for the first time, just regarded as normal.

They would be helped in this, of course, by the general illiteracy of the population. There were no schools, and no opportunity for the vast majority of the population to learn to read or write. The only book in the village would be the Bible, in the church, written in Latin. To put it bluntly, if there is nothing to learn, how can you suffer from a learning disability? It is like that old philosophical conundrum – if a tree falls in a forest, and there is no one within earshot, has it made a sound? I realise this may be stretching it a bit, but I expect you take my point. It may help to explain why Down's syndrome was not recognised until the nineteenth century.

The one section of the population who were literate, or at least had access to learning, were the ruling classes, the Norman aristocracy. The position of the Normans in our history is a strange one, at least for people of my generation (50+) who were brought up to believe that the history of England more or less began with the Norman Conquest. We were taught that these noble people had bestowed upon us a ruling dynasty unmatched in its courage and wisdom, rescuing this miserable island from squalor and elevating us to a position of greatness in the affairs of the world.

Yes, well. The fact is that the Normans were an occupying military power who had seized control of the land and enriched themselves through possessions and taxes. They instituted a fairly brutal rule of martial law to ensure the population stayed quiescent. One of the ways this worked was by establishing the principle of the oath of fealty, whereby groups of men stood surety for each other's behaviour. So, if someone from the village attacked Sir Roger and disappeared, the village would take the consequences. And, knowing the Normans, that would involve torture, flaying, being flung into prison, and jeered at until you died of starvation. It was exactly the same system as used by the Nazis in the Second World War.

This system of law was comprehensive, and not entirely for the benefit of the ruling classes. A villein could sue a lord, for example, and the ordinary population was encouraged to use the law to settle disputes. It gave us the beginnings of property law, among other things. From the Normans onward, the rule of law becomes the cornerstone of our society, its highest mediaeval expression being the Magna Carta, probably the most famous legal document in history.

You may be wondering what the law has to do with disability, but believe it or not this is an important milestone in the history of Down's syndrome. The Normans owned all the land of England, and land meant power, and money. The Norman Lords believed in primogeniture, in passing on their goods and titles to their eldest son. What if that son was disabled, or, even worse, had learning difficulties? What if he had Down's syndrome, and was used by unscrupulous courtiers to dispose of the family fortune? For a people so covetous of material pleasures this would clearly be a disaster, so the law had to be used to protect the family from this occurrence. And to do that, one needed some way of defining the degree of mental incapacity. The idiot was born.

We have no way of knowing how the Normans assessed this disability, but a seventeenth-century legal document describes it thus:

> Idiot is he that is a fool natural from birth and knows not how to account or number twenty pence, nor cannot name his father or mother, nor of what age himself is, or such like easy and common matters; so that it appears he has no manner of understanding or reason, nor government of himself, what is for his profit or pleasure.

For legal purposes, the idiot therefore had no idea of who he was or how to manage his affairs. Fortunately there were people prepared to help, most notably the King, as the thirteenth-century law *Prerogativa Regis* states:

> The king shall have custody of the lands of natural fools taking the profits of them without waste or destruction and shall find them their necessities ... And after the death of such idiots he shall render it to its rightful heirs, so that such idiots shall not alien nor their heirs be disinherited.

You will note that the king kept all the money in the interval.

As the most common cause of congenital learning disability, people with Down's syndrome, especially if they were the eldest male child, would find themselves at the centre of all sorts of property disputes. Can you imagine what it must be like for a Down's syndrome child to have half the room saying you're capable and the other half calling you an idiot? Bear in mind as well that at this time there is no cure for Down's syndrome, no specialist help, and no apparent interest in trying to improve the lot of the sufferer – but there is a law to prove that you are a halfwit.

So, the idiot became legal, and elsewhere, as society developed, the idiot or the fool emerged as a recognisable social and theatrical stereotype. Some of the earliest surviving British plays are the Cornish Ordinalia trilogy, written in the fourteenth century. They tell the story of religion – the origin of the world, the Passion of Christ, and the resurrection – and feature all the major biblical figures, among them God, Abraham, Jesus, Satan, Pilate, and Mary and Joseph. They also field a cast of local characters, soldiers, carpenters and the like, who spice up the text with their simpleton charm and who sometimes mock the exalted. Shakespeare developed the role in some of his works, notably the Fool in *King Lear*. Many European Royal Courts kept a fool, whose role was to say the unsayable, and the fool was often given the task of breaking bad news to the monarch. Fools came in two types, the 'natural' fool, someone congenitally slow witted like a person with Down's syndrome, and the 'licensed' fool, who is more of a jester or comedian, and who would, I suspect, be the fool of preference for the Royal Court. The last people in Britain to employ a court jester were the Bowes-Lyon family, two of whom we met in Earlswood.

Elsewhere in the Middle Ages, there arose the concept of the 'fool for Christ' or holy fool, who challenged people's assumptions by strange or provocative behaviour. Sometimes this involved shedding possessions and living a simple life, although not necessarily joining a monastery or taking holy orders. Some regarded idiots, or 'naturals' as they were sometimes known, as being possessed by the divine spirit because of their simplicity.

The fool, then, or idiot, is beginning to be regarded as different, whether as a sage of licensed jester, or as a man of simple piety. Some fools, that is. I am sure the majority of idiots, including those with Down's syndrome, still led lives of uncomplicated poverty and hardship. But we are, slowly, seeing the emergence of complexity in human character. The wise fool, far from being unworldly and simple, may have been the only sane person around.

This led Sebastian Brant, a German poet, to compose the *Narrenshiff,* or *Ship of Fools*, a book-length narrative poem that mocks more or less everybody in contemporary fifteenth-century culture. There are 114 separate poems, each on a different subject, all of them single versed, and varying from 30 to over 100 lines.

The form is rhyming couplets. Brant had words for every type of man, and woman, and for all the Seven Deadly Sins. He wrote about builders, peasants, fools, gamblers, fallen women and lawyers, and described the follies of pride, greed, gluttony and vanity. Brant wrote about those who revere stupidity:

> It's easy to become a dunce
> And easy to avoid, but once
> A man's become a silly ape
> He'll find it harder to escape.

The *Ship of Fools*, although intended as a satire, quickly became an allegory for the treatment of the mentally ill. Michel Foucault, the French philosopher, imagined the *Ship of Fools*, with its cargo of madmen and idiots, crisscrossing Europe looking for a home, usually being turned away or allowed no further than the quay. The mentally ill were being separated into 'the other', a group of people different from those who were 'normal'. Sometimes this could be seen as a good thing, the simpleton or 'naturelle' being closer to nature and to God. Increasingly, though, the strange and different were not admired, but feared, something to be discouraged in the Europe of the fourteenth to eighteenth centuries. For while we have dwelt on the positives of early mediaeval religious societies, in the libraries and scriptoriums of our religious centres, the Catholic Church was turning inward, and becoming obsessed with the core beliefs of their faith. In particular, the Church sought to destroy those who did not adhere to the increasingly rigid articles of faith, and this boiled down to two groups – heretics and witches. Welcome to the Inquisition.

Strictly speaking, the Inquisition was a mainly European phenomenon, and at a slight tangent to our story, but worth mentioning because its effects are with us today. The problem began in southern France with a religious sect called the Cathars. They believed that the world was evil, and that there were two Gods, Rex Mundi, the King of the World and Lord of Chaos, and another God, a pure spirit, whom they worshipped. Most importantly, because Jesus had appeared in this world, they believed he could not be divine. Their beliefs rejected the acquisition of wealth and power and aimed for spiritual purity, resembling somewhat modern Buddhism. The movement spread rapidly through France and the Catholic Church became concerned, eventually declaring Catharism as a heresy. In 1209, Pope Innocent III authorised the Albigensian Crusade, and knights from northern France and Germany moved to attack the centres of Catharism around Toulouse.

What followed was a massacre. Over the next four years the crusaders besieged city after city, sometimes slaughtering fifty or sixty thousand people. It was one of the first recorded instances of genocide, that is, an attempt to exterminate a people. The leaders of the Cathar movement were burnt at the stake, and many hundreds were killed in the Inquisitions that followed. What made the Inquisition so important was the official sanction for the use of torture to obtain a confession, a morality we still struggle with today.

I said at the start that the relationship with this to our story of Down's syndrome was tangential, and it is, but its significance lies in the developing concept of what is normal and abnormal. We already have divisions of wealth, power, physical and mental abilities. We now have orthodox belief and heresy, and furthermore the understanding that we should not leave unbelievers to themselves, but hunt them down and exterminate them. To be an 'other' in society was becoming dangerous.

Especially for strange women. Although England had its fair share of heretics who were burnt at the stake, the widespread mass imprisonment and torture of continental Europe did not happen here. What we did have, though, were witches.

Witchcraft has a long history, and, like Down's syndrome, has existed in virtually every society since the dawn of humanity. Witches can either use their power for good, as in healing, or evil, by cursing or putting spells on people. Most societies lived in fear of their power, and went out of their way to avoid upsetting the local 'wise woman'. One of the beneficial effects of Christianity was to challenge that power, and free people from the tyranny of superstition. Even so, in rural areas of Britain the superstitions were still alive well into the twentieth century. When I was growing up in Cornwall, a phrase commonly used about poorly looking people was that they were 'wished', that is, ill wished, or cursed.

So, if you were a girl with Down's syndrome who had a particular gift for strange utterances, you might well find yourself subjected to one of the many 'tests' for witchcraft, such as ducking in the village pond, or burning. Mediaeval society had a manual, the *Malleus Maleficarum*, which helped witchfinders identify their prey. This may all sound pretty harmless but the consequences were severe. In Europe it is estimated that twelve thousand witch trials ended with the death penalty. And there were many lesser penalties, including the confiscation of property and wealth.

It is probable that many condemned as witches were actually mentally ill. Those with schizophrenia, acute deliriums, epilepsy, depression, or those with learning difficulties, in fact anyone who appeared to be in the grip of demons, would be candidates for burning. I suspect, however, that the vast majority of witches were not ill, but of a type repressed until the late twentieth century, the independent woman of strong character, not afraid to speak her mind, and quite happy to live on the fringes of society. Maybe, as well, she was a little different, possessed with what the psychiatrists would call a 'strange affect'. The powers that be (that is, men) have always struggled with this type of woman, and it is not long before we start demonising them and hanging all sorts of fantasies on them – mainly sexual, of course, because to become a witch one needed to have intercourse with a demon, and it wasn't only the Romans who let their imaginations run wild. The menace was taken so seriously that a seventeenth-century lawyer, Matthew Hopkins, claimed the title of Witchfinder General, to co-ordinate the extermination of the problem.

Not all outcasts in mediaeval society had fallen foul of the church. Those who had defaulted on their legal obligations, or failed to pay tithes or taxes, could be declared outlaws, 'outwith the law'. This meant they were stripped of their land and properties, which would revert to the Crown. Outlaws were banished from parishes and forced to live in the forests and wild places, where the King's writ did not run. To be declared an outlaw was a serious business, because it meant you were literally worthless – you had no property, no possessions, you were under the threat of death, and if you died your relatives would get nothing.

As well as famous figures like Robin Hood, the forests of England were full of society's outcasts – orphans, the disabled, the poor and the weak. The mentally handicapped, including those with Down's syndrome, would be well represented among them. These bands of dispossessed and desperate men, women and children made the forests dangerous places, shunned by ordinary folk, and the authorities would only enter them in numbers and heavily armed. We have a romantic view of them now, but the reality was somewhat different. John Little and Much the Miller's son were reputed to have killed a monk, and murdered a witness, his page, just for the fun of it.

By the time we reach the sixteenth century, society had com-pletely changed. The idea of personal freedom was taking shape. We had an emerging merchant class, and society was becoming more stratified, including the emergence of an underclass of society's rejects. Education was growing in importance. And in 1536, Henry VIII performed one of the most important acts in British history – he broke from Rome and created the Church of England, with himself as its titular head. In the process he dissolved the monasteries, seizing their wealth and land. And England, gradually, and not without a struggle, became a Protestant coun-try.

The most important administrative district of England became the parish, and the Poor Law of 1601 made it the duty of the parish to provide care for those who were unable to care for themselves. This would include finding accommodation for the mentally ill, and managing the affairs of the incapable, including the disposi-tion of property to provide an income for care. For people with Down's syndrome, this would usually mean living with families or relatives, while 'lunatics' may be sent to specialist houses.

This is another important milestone in the history of Down's syndrome, because it gave the community a statutory duty to care for the poor and disabled in the parish. It had another significant aspect for our purposes, because for the first time records were kept of the number of people qualifying for relief, so we get some idea of the extent of poverty and disability in the community. The parish records were quite specific in their descriptions, which gives us an idea of the types of mental illness. For example, people with learning difficulties were described as 'idiot', 'stupid', 'innocent' or 'natural', whereas others were 'mad', 'lunatic', 'distracted', or 'crazy'.

One thing that emerges from these parish records is the relatively small number of 'idiots' qualifying for relief. The historian Jonathan Andrew thinks that this is not a true reflection of numbers, but rather an indication that people with learning difficulty 'are, and remain, the Cinderella's of the deserving poor'.

Some of the living conditions of the mentally ill were squalid in the extreme. The agitated were often chained up, some for so long that they lost the use of their limbs. One boy of sixteen, admitted to hospital in Germany, 'had lain in the pigpen for years ... and had so lost the use of his limbs and his mind that he lapped food from a bowl, like an animal'. Often the insane were left in their own filth with only the clothes they stood up in, probably eventually dying from disease.

The Reformation saw a profound change in English society, an emergence from the old bucolic Catholic way of life into the sunlit uplands of Protestantism. The historian and *Monty Python* member Terry Jones speculated in his book (with Alan Ereira) *Terry Jones' Mediaeval Lives,* that the old rural Catholic England was actually a pretty good place to live. Dwellings were simple but there was plenty of space. Although villeins had to pay a tithe to the lord and the Church, that probably only took a day out of three or four days' work, and there was plenty of free time in the week. The Church celebrated numerous saints' days, all of which were feasts and holidays. The diet for peasants, rich in cereals and vegetables, was probably better than that of the rich, full of fat and protein. And with nowhere much to go, life was probably more communal, an important factor in the life of someone with a learning disability.

After the creation of the Church of England, life starts to take on the shape we recognise today. The saints' days and holidays were abolished. Much of the fripperies of Catholic belief, the incense and statuary, were swept away, as was much of its art, which meant our artistic heritage was destroyed. The Crown seized the plate and wealth of the Church. The Bible was translated into English, and the Book of Common Prayer replaced the old Latin liturgy, an act which provoked a riot in my native Cornwall ('We will not have this new English for it is like a Christmas game ...'). Elizabethan England traded with the world, and our poets and playwrights, notably Marlowe and Shakespeare, redefined the world of literature. The land was still the major source of employment, but other trades were becoming important, and our towns and cities were taking shape. Society was becoming more stratified, and complex.

At parish level, this complexity saw the emergence of a growing number of people clamouring for relief. It seems that as society became more layered, and more prosperous, it exposed an underclass of the poor and disabled. To qualify for relief, one had to be registered in the parish, and tests of eligibility became more stringent. The main effect of this was to create more homeless and dispossessed, which created further problems. The mentally ill on the fringes of society were as likely to find themselves in gaol as being cared for in suitable surroundings.

And Protestantism, especially in its more extreme forms, was less tolerant of indolence than the old, shrug-your-shoulders Catholicism. If the old church had demonised unbelievers, then the new order added the work-shy and unproductive. The parish was not prepared to pay for people to do nothing, and eventually the workhouse was born, an institution that lasted well into the twentieth century. And, as we have seen, it was not just the work-shy and criminal that got swept into our workhouses and gaols, but the outsiders, the strangers, the sick and unwanted.

But that is at the bottom of society. From the Elizabethan era to the Victorian, England is transformed. We move from an agrarian peasant economy to an industrial one, and citizens desert the countryside to find work in the cities. Learning difficulty is exposed as education becomes widespread. Cromwell challenges the monarchy and kills a king, establishing the basics of Parliamentary rule. The Divine Right of Kings is over. As is the power of the Church, already destroyed by Henry VIII, but now much reduced in its influence over civic affairs. The seventeenth century sees the Age of Enlightenment spread throughout Europe, with science replacing superstition, realism creeping into art, and the rise of the common man in society. The year 1776 sees the American War of Independence, and 1789 the French Revolution. The Western world is throwing off the chains of oppression and becoming free.

So what does this mean for someone with Down's syndrome? How does political change make a difference to someone who may not be able to communicate, and certainly struggles to fit into the new, productive, capitalist world?

The most obvious change is the way society's misfits are left behind as education and prosperity stretch out the rest of society into the highly complex entity it is today. There is no room for the learning disabled or the cripple in the factories and shops of the new England. The companions of the idiot are the outcasts and criminals, still at large in the forests but also roaming the streets of our rapidly expanding cities. Our newly pure Protestant faith is torn between Jesus' call to tend the weak and lowly, and the need to identify and eradicate the work of the devil – 'The devil makes work for idle hands'. The workhouse and the asylum become a practical and moral solution for the deserving and undeserving poor alike.

But, as we enter the asylum era, all is not lost for those with Down's syndrome and the other mentally ill in the community. In particular, parliamentary democracy and liberal capitalism see the emergence of two major beneficial themes.

The first is that having your laws made by Parliament rather than a monarch ensures that all sections of society have a voice. Prior to

1800 there are few laws relating to the care and treatment of the mentally ill. Since then there have been well over fifty laws specifically concerning the provision of care for psychiatric and learning disability cases. From the Victorian era onwards, major advances have been made in the care of those with Down's syndrome. The collective will of the people has been shown to be fairer and more comprehensive than the whims of an absolute monarch (or dictator if we are going to get up to date). We have a healthy cynicism towards our democracy, but sometimes we concentrate so much on what is wrong that we forget the advances that have been made. Up until relatively recent times, the teaching of history in schools concentrated on the actions of kings and left its pupils in the dark about social progress and the life of the common man and woman.

The second beneficial effect of modern capitalism, at least as far as Down's syndrome was concerned, was the growth of Victorian philanthropy, and the creation of specialist centres for people with learning disabilities. Of course it was not comprehensive, and it needed the state to step in and help, but it gave us a start in the quest to provide care for the mentally ill. The great Victorian philanthropists gave us the bricks and mortar, and financed the time of people like Langdon Down, kick-starting the system we have in place today.

Which brings us back to the asylum movement, and the incarceration of the mentally ill. The journey we have so far described for people with Down's syndrome has been an interesting one. Possibly venerated in older times, then ignored, mocked and reviled, then grudgingly accepted, legally defined, then sifted down to the bottom of the heap and finally warehoused into institutions. Over the years they have been treated as badly, if not worse, than any other minority in history. They have truly been the Cinderellas of the deserving poor, quiet, often helpless, ignored and probably abused. But at least they were allowed to live, and nobody sought to hunt them down and exterminate them for what they were.

Unfortunately, all that is about to change. Welcome to the twentieth century.

4

The Twentieth Century

The history of human progress is a strangely staccato affair, delivering advances in art and science not as a smooth progression but in bursts of great creativity. The second half of the nineteenth century, which gave us Marie Curie and Darwin, Dickens and the Brontës, Freud and Pankhurst, among many others, was one of those periods. These geniuses did not live in isolation, but were supported by a pyramid of lesser-known, though equally interesting, thinkers and writers.

One of the most influential Victorian polymaths was the scientist and philosopher Sir Francis Galton, the cousin of Charles Darwin. Like many eminent Victorians, he did not confine his studies to a single subject, but produced ground-breaking work in meteorology, statistics, anthropology, geography, and psychometrics, the study of personality. More importantly for our story, he invented the science of eugenics, the influence of heredity on ability.

Galton studied the families of eminent men and women, and concluded that the upper tier of society were not there by chance, but rose to the top naturally due to a superior genetic make-up. He noted that intelligence was maintained in first-degree relatives, but dropped off proportionately when you got to the second and third degrees. He found that intelligence among offspring declined if the parents had children later in life. This led him to the conclusion that 'man's natural abilities are derived by inheritance ... it would be quite practicable to produce a highly gifted race of men by judicious marriages during several generations'. In other words, you can build a better society by selective breeding.

That was the phenomenon known as positive eugenics. Galton also identified the dark side, negative eugenics, which argued that if you wished to encourage the eminent to procreate and improve the genetic stock, you should also do the opposite, and stop the mentally ill and criminal from producing more social misfits. Galton thought that Darwin's theory of natural selection was 'being thwarted by human civilisation, which protected the weak, and only by changing these policies could society be saved from a reversion to mediocrity'. He believed that 'the applied science (of eugenics) advocates practices aimed at improving the genetic composition of the population'.

To enforce this would obviously require a degree of social control which was impractical for the population as a whole. It was possible, though, for selected groups to marry among themselves, most notably the upper classes, and European royalty in particular. Until relatively recent times it was forbidden for a royal to marry a commoner, an example being the marriage of Prince Charles and Lady Diana Spencer, where the bride was selected on the suitability of her social position and family line as much as anything else.

Eugenics spread rapidly throughout the Western world, and had some prominent supporters, notably George Bernard Shaw, Winston Churchill, H. G. Wells, Marie Stopes, Theodore Rooseveldt, John Kellogg (of corn flakes fame), and the father of British socialism, Sidney Webb. It was in the United States, however, that the movement really took off, or rather, to be strictly accurate, where negative eugenics became an official policy for dealing with social deprivation.

Galton had primarily been a statistician, and the first part of the eugenics movement consisted of identifying the poor genetic stock in society. The first to be categorised were the 'imbeciles', the people with Down's syndrome and other congenital idiots and learning disability cases. Next came the congenitally disabled, those with recognisable disease like cystic fibrosis, plus the blind, the deaf and the spastic. The adult mentally ill were included, not just those with schizophrenia and psychoses, but also those with learning difficulties and the chronically depressed. Normally abled people with criminal or antisocial tendencies, including petty thieves, alcoholics, drug addicts and promiscuous women (not just prostitutes), also found themselves on the list. And finally there were the racial groups thought to be of poor or criminal stock, the Negroes, Gypsies and Jews.

The second part of the movement was its executive branch, which sought socially acceptable solutions to the problem of negative eugenics. Three actions were implemented in the USA: the compulsory sterilisation of those on the register; the forced termination of pregnancies occurring in disadvantaged groups; and the restriction of immigrants from eugenically inferior racial groups. Illinois was the first state, in 1907, to pass a law sanctioning sterilisation for 'imbeciles', and other states rapidly followed suit.

Two organisations were formed in America to further the aims of a eugenic society, the American Breeders Association and the Immigration Restriction League. They collaborated in the founding of the Eugenics Record Office, which opened in New York in 1912 and whose mission statement read:

> Society must protect itself; as it claims the right to deprive the murderer of his life, so it may also annihilate the hideous serpent of hopelessly vicious protoplasm. Here is where appropriate legislation will aid in eugenics and create a healthier, saner society for the future.

Over thirty states passed laws permitting the compulsory sterilisation of the mentally ill and criminal, and by 1960 about 65,000 US citizens had been sterilised under these state acts. One state in particular implemented the policy vigorously. Guess which one – Illinois, perhaps, or some hillbilly paradise like Arkansas or Mississippi? No. California. The most modern and politically correct place on earth was, until 1965, responsible for the forced sterilisation of 20,000 mentally ill or criminal citizens.

The eugenics movement was not solely concerned with the sterilisation of the genetically degenerate or restricting immigration. In the first half of the twentieth century it publicised its aims through nationwide 'Better Baby' competitions, where parents were encouraged to submit their children for examination, who were judged according to their eugenic value. A movement called 'Fitter Families for the Future' also promoted interest in eugenics, examining families' appearance and character traits, and logging the incidence of disability and social problems. Part of the contest included a family questionnaire, an important source of information for the Eugenics Records Office. Families could win medals, and there was considerable social prestige in being rated as 'Grade A'. The race was on to be considered a better family than your neighbours, social competition becoming another characteristic of twentieth-century society.

The downside to this was the scientific separation of 'normal' families, and genetically damaged 'abnormal' families. The person with Down's syndrome was not just unfortunate, they were now corrupted, and considered to be a threat to a healthy society. This is another significant development in the Down's syndrome story, because if people are not considered fully human, then they do not need to be treated in the same way as other human beings. Compassion is the most noble of the virtues to practise, but often the most difficult, and it is all too easily displaced by fear and hatred. In some societies this labelling of the mentally ill became a licence for neglect and abuse.

As well as diffusing through normal society, eugenics became fashionable as a science, and over three hundred colleges in the USA offered eugenics courses. It seems hard for us in the early twenty-first century to understand how something as obviously repellent as the forced sterilisation of individuals could gain such widespread support, but it goes to show how virtually any subject can be sold as desirable, given the right amount of scientific evidence and sympathetic packaging. And there is equally no doubt that, even in our more enlightened times, for some social problems you can easily arrive at eugenics as the answer.

In case you think that I am being unduly pessimistic, I will recount a story from my time as a GP in rural England in the late twentieth century. Every week we would have a Primary Health Care Team meeting, where the doctors, practice nurses, health visitors, midwives, district nurses and social workers would meet and discuss challenging cases. Although a wide range of the practice patients passed through the meeting, a pattern began to emerge. It was apparent that we had a hard core of families, probably no more than four or five out of six thousand patients, who, generation after generation, were not only trapped in the lowest tier of society, but actively ensured its survival. The men would be alcoholics and vicious bullies, the women mean-eyed and nasty, and the household abusive and dirty. The children would be neglected, escaping at the earliest opportunity, the boys to become drug addicts and often violent criminals, and the girls to be teenage single mothers who went from relationship to relationship. The children often ended up in care, graduating to prison, and you knew that the best they could hope for was a life on benefits. At every turn in their lives they made the wrong decision. The cost to the state was vast, probably over a lifetime running to hundreds of thousands of pounds (a current estimate has it at over £500,000). Children of four or five were coming to the surgery having had more horror in their short lives than most of us experience in a lifetime.

None of us had heard of eugenics, but more than once we speculated, only half jokingly, that the sterilisation of a few individuals would prevent a series of ruined lives, cut the crime rate dramatically, and save the country an awful lot of money. And if, as I suspect it will, we find society struggling with the cost of social deprivation, you may find that 'socially responsible pregnancy', or something similar, will see a form of eugenics become fashionable again.

And those types of sentiments accounted for the success of the early eugenics movement. If you are in a society struggling to cope with a burgeoning underclass and have no other means of birth control, then forced sterilisation must seem like the obvious answer. There are also, as well, practical problems to be considered, most notably the care of children conceived by someone with florid mental health or social problems. A girl with severe Down's syndrome is incapable of looking after herself, let alone a child, and it is not difficult to argue that sterilisation prevents a life of misery for her and her offspring. And, of course, if society is picking up the pieces then some of our more authoritarian politicians are going to argue that society should call the tune.

In the USA and Canada, both of whom were the destination for millions of immigrants, another problem became apparent. Who were their preferred new citizens? Who provided the most value to the emerging power of the United States of America? The Immigration Restriction League was already arguing that America could not allow unfettered immigration, because of the perceived corruption of the gene pool. A 'Racial Hierarchy' was drawn up which listed the races in order of preference and which went Anglo Saxon, European, Oriental and, finally, Negro. People with Down's syndrome, and other congenital idiots, were already at the bottom of the pile in early twentieth-century America, and here they were joined by the African Americans. Forced sterilisation of the mentally ill was already in place, and it was rumoured that there was a covert eugenics programme for black Americans, the Negro Project Conspiracy Theory. We can see the layers of twentieth-century society developing.

As well as sterilising patients with Down's syndrome, several states prohibited the marriage of 'imbeciles', and some also denied them the vote, an act still in force in some US states, although most of them are not enforced and are now generally regarded as anachronisms.

In the context of the wider world, it was not just the USA which had a eugenics programme. Canada had one, as did Australia (focusing mainly on the Aborigines), Sweden, Japan, China, Finland, Denmark, Iceland, Switzerland and France. The most notorious, and shameful, use of eugenics took place in Nazi Germany, where the disabled were actively persecuted, a story we will come to shortly.

For the person with Down's syndrome, the twentieth century so far seems to have been a time of unremitting misery. From the high point of the late nineteenth century Enlightenment, when pioneers like Down actively sought to improve the lot of those with learning difficulties, the person with Down's syndrome has been shoved to the bottom of the pile, warehoused, forcibly sterilised, and isolated. The society that tried to help them has rejected them, and worse, deprived them of the few human rights they could exercise. It was as if the disabled were a problem people would rather do without, and preferred to hide away. And this now brings us back to the asylum, where most people with Down's syndrome were living.

When we left the nineteenth century, the idea of the asylum as a therapeutic centre was withering as the numbers of mentally ill increased exponentially. What we would now call the 'care pathway' for Down's syndrome was simple – diagnosis, removal from the family, and incarceration in an asylum, hopefully one for learning disabilities, but if not, any asylum, however inappropriate.

The living conditions in asylums in the early twentieth century were deteriorating. The doubling, and even tripling, of numbers in asylums over the nineteenth century had led to severe overcrowding. Colney Hatch, in North London, had 2,200 beds, but at one point housed over 3,500 patients. Institutional life is, at best, just about acceptable, but overcrowded institutional life is intolerable, both for patients and staff. Some hospitals in the United States were even larger, like Milledgeville asylum in the state of Georgia, which housed 10,000 patients.

There was still a separation into learning disabilities and psychiatric hospitals, although the boundaries were blurred, and a patient with Down's syndrome could end up in either. Conditions were changing in both due to the inability of therapeutic regimes to provide a service for the increased numbers of patients. The old psychiatric institutes, especially in Germany, were run on family lines, where each patient was part of a socially cohesive unit, but that was now impossible. The numbers were so great that staff and patients had to wear separate uniforms to identify them, making the asylums appear more like prisons. This was reinforced by the drab décor, the chocolate browns, slime green and noisome yellow, which have become the favoured colour scheme for our institutions.

Inside, life had become grim. Most asylums catering for the genuinely insane were horrible, with the incessant crying and screaming and gibbering of the patients making it almost impossible to think. Smearing the walls with excrement was still a common practice, as was open masturbation. If you were lucky, you might be sharing accommodation with someone mildly eccentric or simply criminal, if not you might be with someone suffering from paranoid schizophrenia or a psychosis. The inmates of Colney Hatch included John Duffy, a serial rapist and killer, Aaron Kosminski, a Jack the Ripper suspect, and the exotically named Maria Teresa Ferrari de Miramar, one of Aleister Crowley's wives.

Although generally the state of asylums was bad, in some respects the conditions for patients had improved. One of the functions of the warders was to protect the vulnerable from the more dangerous patients, which, although not perfect, at least made the asylums a little safer. And they were much cleaner than the nineteenth-century asylums, many of the newer ones being purpose built. Segregation of dirty patients, and the creation of specialist, wash-down cells, improved conditions for other inmates.

And it was possible for the patient's stay to be relatively short. Many acute psychiatric conditions remitted spontaneously, and if that happened the patients were discharged. There was quite a high turnover of younger patients with acute psychiatric disease, and because of pressure of numbers, if there was a hint of normality the patient was freed. So although there was nothing approaching a cure for any of the conditions, there was still the possibility that one's stay might be measured in weeks, except, of course, for one group of patients, whose identity I suspect you have guessed – the 'congenital idiots'. The 'care pathway' for Down's syndrome and learning disabilities was now lifelong institutionalisation.

The horror of our mental hospitals made the early twentieth-century psychiatrists increasingly desperate to find cures for the wide range of intractable psychiatric conditions, and in the absence of specific psychiatric drugs a number of solutions were attempted. The Viennese psychiatrist Wagner-Juaregg found that fever caused the symptoms of syphilis to remit. He tried treating patients with neurosyphilis with tuberculin, and gained some success, but the experiment had to be abandoned because of the toxicity of tuberculin. He later used the blood of patients infected with malaria, which was important because malaria could be cured with quinine. Then, in the 1930s, along came penicillin, and syphilis became the first psychiatric disease curable by drugs alone.

Other patients were not so lucky, particularly those with behavioural problems, whose problems were difficult to manage and who were therefore at the cutting edge of early psychiatric experimentation. One of the first attempts at therapy was the sleep cure, where barbiturates or bromide were used to produce a prolonged coma for up to six or seven days. This seemed to be effective for adult patients who had suddenly developed psychosis or mania. The problem was, it was not without risk – patients could aspirate stomach contents and develop pneumonia, or even die. An overdose of the drugs would kill you, and barbiturates were addictive. But at last some patients were getting better as a result of externally applied treatment.

A much more effective refinement of the sleep cure was insulin therapy, where coma was induced by injecting the hormone insulin to cause a rapid reduction in blood sugar. The profound coma which ensued 'created a new being', according to one of the psychiatric observers. The coma had to be repeated up to twenty times to be effective, but the results were encouraging. Over 50 per cent of patients experienced significant relief from their symptoms, a staggering success by the standards of the time.

Patients who went into insulin coma frequently suffered from convulsions, and the next great advance in psychiatry was to see if the induction of epileptic fits could cause a change in the patient's mood. A Hungarian doctor, Ladislas von Meduna, induced a fit in a

37-year-old man with schizophrenia by injecting the drug cardiazol. The man had been an inpatient for four years, spending the
first year hiding under his bedclothes, and the rest of the time
mostly cut off from any form of human contact. After a two-week
course of five injections he woke up and asked where he was, and
was astonished to find that he had been in a psychiatric hospital for
four years. Shortly afterwards he washed, got dressed, and left the
hospital, never to return.

Dramatic though these cures could be, many patients refused to
have cardiazol a second time because of its side effects, which were
a premonition of impending death, and the feeling that they were
crumbling away. The psychiatric profession looked for alternatives,
and it was an Italian physician, Ugo Cerletti, who postulated that
electricity could be used to induce convulsions, inventing the
discipline of Electroconvulsive Therapy or ECT. ECT was effective
for adult psychosis and delusional states, but also for patients with
profound depression, for which it is still used today. Convulsive
therapy seemed to break down acquired patterns of negative
thinking, although nobody really knows how it works, even now.
Still, progress was being made.

All these advances took place in the 1930s, which is really where
the story of modern psychiatry begins. Unfortunately none of
these advances would make a difference to Down's syndrome
patients, although it is almost certain that they would have been
subjected to some of them, especially if they were depressed or
suffering from behavioural difficulties. The important thing to
grasp here, though, is the notion that at long last psychiatry could
do something active for its patients. The dark side of this was the
increasing dehumanisation of the psychiatric patient, first by ware-
housing them, and then by regarding them in much the same way
as you would a laboratory rat. It wasn't going to be long, unfortunately, before 'doing something active' took on a whole new
meaning.

In 1932, Adolf Hitler became Chancellor of Germany, introduc-
ing the politics of National Socialism to a world ravaged by the First
World War and ruined by the great depression. One of the aims of

Nazism was to restore the supremacy of the Aryan race, reversing what Hitler saw as the catastrophic dilution of pure German blood by intermarriage with other, lesser races. The establishment of the Third Reich also included the reclamation of territory Hitler believed to be historically German, now overrun by the *untermenschen*, the Slavs and Poles and others considered to be inferior to the master race. Allied to this was the need to confront the forces destabilising Germany, the international conspiracy of Jews who controlled the world's finances, and the Bolsheviks mustering in the east.

In a Germany rocked by the poverty and squalor of the Weimar Republic these were attractive ideas, especially the thought that you belonged to a master race brought low by genetic pollution. Equally, believing that you are on the wrong end of a conspiracy never fails to attract support among the disadvantaged. In 1903 the Russian Secret Service forged a document called *The Protocols of the Elders of Zion*, which detailed the alleged Jewish conspiracy to take over the world. It contained details of how to control the world's financial markets, the world's press, and how to corrupt the morals of the Gentiles. Numerous influential figures on both sides of the Atlantic believed it to be true – Henry Ford actually had extra copies printed – and it reinforced the entrenched anti-Semitism which lay below the surface of Western society. Hitler believed it implicitly, and exploited it ruthlessly, using his masterful rhetoric to inflame his brutal followers.

The idea of an 'Aryan race', a distinct branch of human ancestry descended from the Indo-European races, had its origin in the work of nineteenth-century anthropologists. This idea was taken on by the anthropologist Arthur de Grobineau, who argued that the races were not equal, but could be arranged in a hierarchy according to abilities, with the Aryan being superior to the Anglo Saxon, Oriental, Negro, Aboriginal, and so on. Hitler was a firm believer in Aryan superiority, and was obsessed by Nietzsche's theory of the *Übermensch*, the 'Overman' or Superman, who was the next stage in human evolution, being as far above a human being as a human was from an ape. It was thought that this super race could be created 'breeding upwards', in other words selecting fit and healthy, genetically pure, specimens from a chosen people and encouraging them to procreate. Hitler believed that the race chosen to breed the *Übermensch* was the Aryan race, that is, the German people, later expanded to include the Dutch and Scandinavians. Pure Aryan marriages were encouraged and given financial support from the state, and abortion for women carrying pure Aryan children was forbidden. The programme was a partial success, because although we did not get the *Übermensch*, it did produce the stereotype of the big, powerful, blond-haired warrior of popular myth.

The downside of this was that there was no room for the imperfect in such a society. Posters began appearing showing the disabled, notably those with hereditary illness, saying, 'This man costs the state 60,000 Reich marks in his lifetime. Fellow citizens, this is your money!' The clamour to do something about the dispossessed, the feeble, the outsiders, all those who might pollute the master race, had begun.

Hitler had explained, in *Mein Kampf*, his attitude to the disabled, which was more or less upon eugenic lines, and one of his first acts in government was to pass the 'Law for the Prevention of Hereditary Diseased Offspring', a compulsory sterilisation programme which affected 400,000 people. The more extreme elements of the eugenics movement in the United States had already advocated the state killing of those with intractable congenital problems, so the intellectual ground had been prepared for what followed next. Hitler had already argued that the most severely affected people with congenital illnesses should be 'spared more suffering', but the hierarchy of the party were nervous about what was, in effect, state murder. It was also true that such a measure, if made public, would have incurred the disapproval of the Catholic Church, still a power in Germany in the mid 1930s, and an organisation Hitler could not afford to offend.

He continued to advocate mercy killing privately, and in 1939 was given a boost by the parents of a severely disabled boy, Gerhard Kretschmar, who publicly petitioned Hitler asking for their son to be put to death to end his suffering. Hitler granted this, and set up the Reich Committee for the Scientific Registering of Serious Hereditary and Congenital Illnesses, in order to identify the extent of the problem. Privately, he organised a group of physicians to carry out his true wishes. On 1 September 1939 he wrote the following directive:

> Reich leader Bouhler and Dr Brandt are charged with the responsibility for expanding the authority of physicians, to be designated by name, to the end that patients considered incurable according to the best available human judgement (*menschlichem Ermessen*) of their state of health can be granted a mercy death (*Gnadentod*).

Action T4, the state euthanasia programme dealing with disabled and mentally ill adults and children, was born. The letter was handwritten, and did not circulate among the rest of his ministers, and was therefore an illegal act, marking the descent of Nazi Germany into outright criminality. It was the first time that a legally constituted democratic state had authorised the killing of disabled people, with Down's syndrome sufferers being its principal victims.

T4 was the name of a villa in the Berlin suburbs, Tiergartenstrabe 4, which was the headquarters of the Charitable Foundation for Cure and Institutional Care, the somewhat ironic title of the organisation responsible for selecting the victims. From 1939, the Interior Ministry required doctors and midwives to report abnormal births and children. The conditions included idiocy, Down's syndrome, microcephaly, hydrocephalus, spasticity and all deformities. The children were examined by a panel of doctors, who theoretically decided which of the afflicted would be selected. In practice, they all were. The parents were not told that they were going to be killed, but rather sent to a centre for 'special treatment'. The killing did not start until the war had begun, because even the Nazis realised they could not get away with it in peacetime. The children were killed by lethal injection, although that changed when drugs became expensive, and the gas chamber became the preferred method of execution. Again, the parents were not told of the true cause of death, but informed that their children had died of 'pneumonia' or some other natural cause.

It is probable that most of the parents would not have given their consent for the child's removal had they known what was going to happen. Some of us might wonder how they could have been that naive, given Hitler's publicly stated views on the disabled, but we have to remember that Nazi Germany was a police state where defiance of authority usually meant imprisonment and torture. Also, the collapse of the German economy prior to Hitler had led to the contraction of health services, with care for learning disabilities now being low priority. The asylums were over-crowded, and those looking after seriously disabled children at home probably had a life of constant toil. On the face of it, here was a source of relief, and it would have been foolish to reject it. Within a year or two, however, even the fig leaf of parental consent was stripped away, and children were simply taken away and killed.

We do not know exactly how many were murdered. Official records show that between 70,000 and 90,000 children were killed from 1939 to 1941, when the programme was suspended. The figure may well be much higher. In one centre alone, Schloss Hartheim, over 8,000 children were put to death. To put this in perspective, imagine if all the disabled children you knew simply disappeared. And what must it have been like to work in such a place? What did the workers there believe they were doing to those poor children? Surely something must have registered, some vestigial part of their conscience must have known what they were doing was wrong? It is the question you always come up against when discussing this problem: how could ordinary people – because by and large they were ordinary people – do such things?

In any other time, this would have been mass murder on a grand scale. In the Second World War, in the death camps of Poland and Germany, the extermination of the learning disabled was a mere footnote to the genocide of the Jews. About 6 million Jews were murdered in the death camps, along with homosexuals, Gypsies,

Jehovah's Witnesses, the adult mentally ill, the disabled and prisoners of war. In all, between 11 and 17 million people were killed.

Not all were simply starved to death or gassed, either. The Nazis
used the death camps for medical experiments, testing the effects
of drugs, hypoxia and impact injuries on prisoners. Some were
operated on without anaesthetic, having organs like the stomach,
or even the heart, removed. If they survived they were killed
anyway. In some of the atmospheric experiments, for example the
effect of low pressure or hypoxia, the aim of the experiment was to
see at what point the patient died. As someone who spent thirty
years as a doctor, I cannot write this without feeling sick. There is
nothing worse than high intelligence allied to bestial cruelty,
because unlike the madman, these people knew exactly what they
were doing. Fortunately, I think the majority of Down's syndrome
patients were simply killed, not experimented on, but we can
never know for sure.

The Nazis were a stain on humanity, but they were not unique in
the twentieth century in their desire to eradicate problem citizens.
A bit further east, Josef Stalin had instituted the 'Great Terror',
which saw 11–20 million of the Soviet Union's citizens dying in the
gulags and prisons of the USSR. It is not clear how Stalin viewed the
disabled, and there certainly does not appear to be a Soviet
programme like Action T4, where the disabled are selected for
execution, but it is likely that some Down's syndrome patients
would have passed through the camps.

Germany and the USSR are the two names that spring to mind
when the forced extermination of minorities, and whole races, are
concerned. However, between 1914 and 1950, genocide occurred
in the following countries: Turkey, USSR, Croatia, Dominican
Republic, Germany, India and China. Perhaps what is more disturbing is the number of countries in which genocide has taken
place since 1951: Australia, Zanzibar, Pakistan, Guatemala,
Rwanda, Burundi, Guinea, Cambodia, East Timor, Argentina, Leba-
non, Afghanistan, Ethiopia, Iraq, Yugoslavia, Brazil, Congo, Papua
New Guinea, and Somalia. Genocide has been practised throughout history, but never to the extent that it has in the twentieth

century. And the problem in the twentieth century is that when one is considering undesirable minorities, the disabled come perilously close to the top of the pile. Even if they are not specifically targeted, one doesn't need much imagination to guess that they may be 'accidentally' swept up in the purges.

At the end of the Second World War, two conflicting ideologies controlled most of the world's landmass – the capitalist West, including the USA and half of Europe, and the communist East, the USSR, Eastern Europe and, later, China. The two blocs lived in a state of mutual hostility, the Cold War, which erupted into open conflict in Korea and Vietnam. Probably only the threat of nuclear annihilation prevented a third world war. Both had very different economic systems, and different approaches to healthcare. Were there any differences between the systems as far as Down's syndrome was concerned?

In the West, as we have seen, the preferred approach was to institutionalise people with learning difficulties, in hospitals which provided basic care but little else. In the USSR, a socialised healthcare system was introduced after the Revolution, which guaranteed free healthcare to all citizens. A much wider range of childcare provision was available in the USSR, with children encouraged to attend specialist nurseries and day schools. The state took over many of the functions of the traditional three-generation Russian family, a policy represented in the West as an attempt to destroy family life. This may have resulted in better care for children with Down's syndrome , who before would have just lived at home with their families, probably in poverty. It is likely that the general health of the population improved due to the increased availability of doctors and medicines, and more perhaps than we in the West would give credit for. Certainly, Soviet infant mortality statistics show an improvement in the first years of Communist rule. Successive Five Year Plans set out to improve both the quantity and quality of healthcare. In the Soviet Union, and each of the constituent countries of the Eastern Bloc, there existed provision for the disabled, including a system of classification into fully and partially disabled, and an extensive remuneration package. This took place against the backdrop of industrialisation and the collectivisation of the farms that led to the social upheavals, famine and unrest which killed so many Soviet citizens. Allied to this was the all-pervasive secrecy and paranoia, which saw dissidents removed from their homes at night and taken away, never to be seen again. It is possible that this was the fate of the disabled and learning disabilities patients who did not fit the model of the ideal Soviet citizen, and it seems that until recently there were special labour camps for the disabled.

One needs to add qualification here that it is quite hard to find out the truth about the disabled in the USSR. The traditional Western view was that life under Communism was brutal, oppressive, and poor, and that life in the West was infinitely superior. On the other hand, it seems that Russia did have a system of comprehensive social and medical care from the 1930s onwards, which may have been better than many in the West experienced. Many Western writers and thinkers clearly believed it was so, and were desperate for Russia to be some sort of Utopia, just as the capitalist class wanted to portray it as a giant prison. The truth, as always, lies somewhere in between.

What is certain is that in the post-war period, both sides in the Cold War, but especially the Russians, started using psychiatry to break the will of 'normal' people, who were dissidents, traitors or spies. The methods used were psychological, sleep deprivation and torture, and pharmacological, using drugs like scopolamine to induce confessions. A prolonged spell in a Russian gaol under the attentions of the KGB left many people with irreversible psychiatric problems – those that were allowed to live, that is. There is probably equally no doubt that the same thing occurred in the West, although on a much reduced scale. So we now have a new phenomenon in the history of psychiatry, the deliberately induced psychiatric illness. There was also a new diagnosis, sluggish schizophrenia, where the patient exhibits antisocial tendencies, paranoia and mistrust of the authorities. The 'sufferers' were the intellectuals, dissidents and artists who had come to the conclusion that they were living in a dystopia. Patients so diagnosed were admitted under the joint care of the Russian psychiatry service and the KGB. It is unlikely that people with Down's syndrome were sent to the KGB cells, but as our story has followed the history of psychiatry, the abuse of psychiatry is worth mentioning for the sake of completeness.

We have now reached the 1960s and the story of Down's syndrome is about to change radically. The twentieth century has poor children with Down's syndrome taken from their homes, institutionalised, and left to rot in crumbling Victorian sanatoria along with similarly afflicted inmates. And those are the lucky ones – the less fortunate are sterilised, forbidden to marry, thrust into violent and dirty asylums, and regarded as non-human. And then there are the ones who grow up in totalitarian societies, or in countries where war leads to genocide, where they get put to death just for who they are. The story of our treatment of the disabled and disadvantaged has reached its darkest hour.

Fortunately, we are standing on the brink of another of those great ages in human development, the second half of the twentieth century. The 1960s are upon us, and with it a revolution in our cultural, social and political lives. In medicine, a group of radical thinkers is poised to change the face of psychiatry and learning disabilities for ever. The Age of Aquarius is dawning, and in the words of one of its anthems, from the 1960s musical *Hair*, 'Let the sun shine in.'

5

The New Enlightenment

At first glance, the controversial English politician Enoch Powell would appear to be an unlikely character in the Down's syndrome story. Powell achieved fame, and notoriety, for his famous 1968 speech on the dangers of uncontrolled immigration, which he ended by quoting the poet Virgil: 'Like the Roman, I seem to see "the River Tiber foaming with much blood".' The 'Rivers of Blood' speech defined his public persona and ensured that he became a demonic figure for some, and a sort of folk hero for others. Not the sort of person, one would imagine, who had a lot of time for minorities.

Our interest lies with his time as a Health Minister, when he proved to be an able if controversial legislator. In 1961 he gave a landmark address to the National Association for Mental Health in which he criticised asylums and their place in society, a speech which became known as the 'water tower' speech:

> There they stand isolated, majestic, imperious, brooded over by the gigantic water tower and chimney combined, the asylums which our forefathers built ... to express the notions of the day. Do not doubt for a moment their powers of resistance to our assault.

Powell's plan was for long-stay psychiatric hospitals to be phased out, to be replaced by community care – 'nothing less than the elimination of by far the greater part of this country's mental hospitals as they stand today'. The story of healthcare has been littered with wildly inaccurate speculation about the future, but this statement is one of the few predictions made about health that has actually come true. No longer do our cities house the brooding asylums of yesteryear, the 'water tower' palaces of shame and fear, to be talked about in hushed whispers. When I was growing up in Cornwall in the 1960s the County Asylum was in Bodmin, and everyone knew that being 'sent to Bodmin' meant being locked away behind the walls of that grim Victorian institution. Nor was it a joke, like so many things in the country are, but something to be hidden and feared.

Enoch Powell was not, however, a lone visionary, but was drawing on the legislative and scientific advances which had been made during and after the Second World War. The Welfare State had its origins in the Lloyd George government of 1911, which provided national insurance for unemployment and sickness, but it was the social reformer William Beveridge who provided the framework for post-war Britain. The key document in the planning of services was the Beveridge Report, published in 1942, which dealt with social insurance and allied services, and which became the template for social care in Britain for the rest of the century. It advocated a National Insurance scheme for the funding of health and social care, and introduced the universal child benefit, among other reforms.

But by far the most important advance, not just for learning difficulties but also for all healthcare in Britain, was the creation, in 1948, of the National Health Service. The NHS was unique in the Western world at the time in offering healthcare 'to all citizens, according to need, free at the point of delivery'. The scope and ambition of this project was unmatched by any other capitalist country, and though the NHS has suffered conflicting fortunes since, nothing can detract from the nobility of its founding principles.

A detailed discussion about the NHS is beyond the scope of this book, but what it meant for Down's syndrome patients was the theoretical integration of care into a wider social structure. This began with taking the old 'incurable' and 'idiot' hospitals into the NHS, and then replacing haphazard private provision with more appropriate care. The provision of healthcare through central planning and funded by general taxation meant that for the first time Britain could theoretically construct a nationwide collective health service.

The problems of day-to-day living also saw the creation of benefits specifically for people with disability, an often complex process which has culminated in the Disability Living Allowance, a non-means-tested untaxed benefit for disabled people under 65.

In the voluntary sector, amalgamating three other charities formed the National Association of Mental Health (later MIND), and it rapidly became a powerful advocate for the mentally ill. The immediate post-war years saw the beginnings of a revolution in the care of the mentally ill of all types.

The creation of the NHS occurred at a time of great change in psychiatry, with doctors beginning to consider the possibility of community care for psychiatric and learning difficulty patients. The problem remained of the potential dangers of a patient having a violent relapse in an unsafe setting, where innocent people may get hurt. Until the 1940s there was no physical or psychological therapy which could prevent this from happening. Then, almost overnight, along came the one development that made the care of the mentally ill in the community a reality. And strangely enough it is not a person, or a theory, or an institution, or a machine, but a single small pill – the drug Largactil.

If the physical treatments of the 1930s had transformed psychiatry, then Largactil, or chlorpromazine as it is properly called, provided a pharmacological revolution. The drug was introduced in the 1940s, and suddenly patients prone to severe behavioural difficulties could take a tablet which controlled their often violent mood swings. This meant that not only did their clinical condition improve, but their care was easier, making community care a real possibility.

This was aided by legislation which encouraged local authorities to provide facilities for 'persons who, by reason of age, illness, disability, or other circumstances, are in need of care and attention which is not otherwise available to them'. In the 1950s, day hospitals were established which produced greater flexibility in the care of psychiatric and learning disability patients. Outpatient nurses were provided to help the step-down care for patients discharged from psychiatric hospitals. After rising inexorably for the whole of the twentieth century, psychiatric inpatient numbers began to decline. This was a widespread phenomenon in the Western world, occurring despite significant differences in the structure and funding of individual health services. The process was inexorable, but painfully slow, and the first closure of a major psychiatric hospital in England had to wait until 1988.

The watershed document for Down's syndrome patients was the 1957 'Royal Commission on the law relating to mental illness and mental deficiency.' The primary recommendation of the Commission was that 'the law should be altered so that wherever possible care may be provided for mentally disordered patients with no more restriction of liberty or legal formality than is applied to people who need care because of other types of illness, disability, or social difficulty'. The Commission also recommended that 'the majority of mentally ill patients do not need to be admitted to hospitals as inpatients. Patients can receive medical treatments from general practitioners or as hospital outpatients, and other care from community services.'

Some very significant advances are contained in these legislative and organisational initiatives. First, and most importantly, it is recognised that large numbers of those labelled as mentally ill do not need to be in hospital, and that appropriate care can be provided in the community. For once, this is an advance that benefits Down's syndrome patients more than the general psychiatric community, because they were one group of patients whose presence in psychiatric institutions was largely for historic reasons.

It is, of course, no use discharging patients into the community if there is nowhere for them to go, otherwise you end up back in the seventeenth century. The second great advance was the legal requirement for local authorities to provide suitable care for former psychiatric inpatients in the community. This has been a process fraught with complications, not least because of the difficulties in predicting the course of psychiatric disease, but it was a huge improvement on what happened before. Similarly, the creation of day-care facilities, and the introduction of community psychiatric nurses provided a practical support network for both the psychiatric and learning disability patients who were sent back to the community. Finally, there was the magic bullet, chlorpromazine, which enabled previously dangerous patients to be rehabilitated with some degree of comfort.

In the wider world, the face of psychiatry was changing, reflecting the counter-culture attitudes of the 1960s. One the most influential thinkers was the French philosopher,Michel Foucault, who published the seminal work *Madness and Civilisation* in 1961. It is a difficult book to sum up in a short paragraph as it is wide ranging, speculative, and full of literary allusion, but it contains two very interesting concepts. The first is that madness became a problem as civilisation evolved, replacing leprosy as society's demonic disease. The strange and mad, the seers and simpletons, who had been an accepted part of the community in pre-Reformation times, suddenly became different, and a threat to normal society. Foucault argued that the early psychiatrists like Pinel, far from attempting to 'cure' madness, were in fact forcing the disturbed outsider to conform to the values of 'normal' society. Given what we know about the state of some of the asylums, there is a grain of truth in this concept.

The other great name of the anti-psychiatry movement in Britain was the Scottish psychiatrist R. D. Laing. Laing was an existentialist who brought a unique intelligence to the discipline of psychiatry, in particular the problems of psychosis and schizophrenia. His theories are complex, but interesting, especially for those of us who agree with Sartre's observation that 'hell is other people'. One of Laing's theories was the idea that different people have different views of us as an individual, fine if the person is 'ontologically sound' (or 'together' as we would say now) but a source of unresolvable conflict, mental illness, if they are not. He believed that the hallucinations of the person with schizophrenia were, to the patient, real experiences, and may have had some protective function. Although Laing and Foucault recognised that 'madness' as an entity existed, they thought it was over-diagnosed, stemming from society's discomfort with the outsider.

The anti-psychiatry movement was also prominent in the USA, where the psychiatrist Thomas Szasz wrote *The Myth of Mental Illness*, in which he argued that the idea of psychiatric illness was 'socially harmful and scientifically worthless'. A sociologist, Erving Goffman, studied asylums and came to the conclusion that they infantilised patients, at every stage emphasising the difference between 'abnormal' patients and 'normal' staff. Foucault, Szasz, Laing and Grossman had a profound effect on the intellectual atmosphere of the 1960s.

But it was not the intellectual atmosphere that changed the public perception of psychiatry. The event which did, according to Professor Shorter in his *History of Psychiatry*, was the book *One Flew over the Cuckoo's Nest*, written by a former psychiatric nurse, Ken Kesey. It tells the story of a drifter, Randle McMurphy, who, although not psychiatrically ill, does not fit into society either, and who eventually gets incarcerated in a psychiatric hospital. It was made into a film in 1974, starring Jack Nicholson, and profoundly affected those who saw it, myself among them. The film portrayed institutional life as one long attempt to get the patients to conform, the staff eventually lobotomising McMurphy as a final attempt to control his behaviour. For people in the 1970s, living in a society infused with the paranoia of the Cold War, this was a viscerally frightening experience. We all believed it to be true, and when some of us in the medical profession ventured onto the psychiatric wards, we found that a lot of it *was* true. In defence of psychiatry, it should be said that the public think that controlling the behaviour of the mad person is the psychiatrist's first duty, and any failure on that part invites the full fury of the press and public alike.

Back in the heady days of the 1960s, however, the mission was to change the world. As someone who lived through those times, I recall that there was a very real sense of revolution, of rejecting everything the previous generation had stood for. If the boring old men who ran the country thought that locking up the mentally ill was right, then we would do the opposite, and set them free. And, to be fair, the spirit of the counter-culture had a lot to work with – in the Western world, and Britain in particular, events were ritualised to the point of insanity, done that way 'because that is the way they have always been done'. The twenty years after the war had also seen the West, particularly American society, enthusiastically embrace the consumer culture, the pursuit of material wealth replacing softer values as the driving force behind many people's lives. The hippies and other outsiders rejected all this, and often went back to a simpler, more communal style of living. The past was rejected, and everything had to change.

As in so many political upheavals, the last people to be consulted on the course of events were the ones who were meant to profit from them. Although no one can now argue that we should send Down's syndrome patients back into the asylums, at the time, the release from hospital was not an unalloyed pleasure. Many of the old psychiatric hospitals had provided suitable work for their patients, with farm work and arts and crafts being popular vocations. Although not therapeutic, in the strictly medical sense of the word, they provided structure and order and care, all things which could be lacking in the outside world. Order and routine create the institutionalised mentality, so when they vanish, being in an otherwise stable environment is disorientating. For the person with schizophrenia or a psychosis, who is on medication, there was also the realisation that drugs like Largactil came with some serious side effects, among them lethargy, disordered mental function and Parkinson's disease. For Down's syndrome patients, they were exposed to a society which thought they were freaks, and which mixed kindness and vilification. Release was not a pleasant experience for many of our psychiatric inmates.

In the wider medical world, the second half of the twentieth century saw an explosion in medical knowledge, treatment and technology. Major advances were made in virtually every speciality, and medicine today is unrecognisable from the medicine of the 1960s. One of the specialities which saw the biggest advance was that of anaesthetics, where new drugs and machines made it possible to keep patients anaesthetised for much longer. This in turn revolutionised the practice of surgery, making complex operations much safer. Muscle relaxant drugs made abdominal operations like stomach ulcer and gallbladder surgery technically easier, and they became routine procedures. Obstetrics also benefited, with Caesarian sections, previously a particularly fraught operation, becoming considerably less stressful. Joint replacement became commonplace. More importantly, there was the introduction of new fields like cardiac surgery, making it possible to repair congenital defects and damaged arteries.

If the growth in surgery in the post-war period was impressive, the evolution of pharmacology was nothing short of explosive. The fifty years since 1960 have seen drug treatments for disease rise exponentially. Major advances have been made in virtually every disease category, from heart disease to cancer. Examples of drugs which we take for granted now but didn't exist in 1960 are:

    for asthma – inhalers
    for heart disease – statins, ACE inhibitors, beta blockers
    for infections – virtually every antibiotic
    for diabetes – commercial insulin and the drugs for Type 2 diabetes
    for cancer – virtually all the chemotherapeutic agents.

The list of drugs, the formulary, available in 1960, was the size of a small pamphlet, and many of the drugs were little better than placebo – 'Dr Pepper's Pink Pills', for example, which were a hangover from Victorian times and were little more than vaguely therapeutic Smarties. The formulary today is the size of a small encyclopaedia, and every drug has passed through stringent tests as to its efficacy. There is hardly a medical condition which is not treatable with something.

This applies to psychiatry as much as anything. Where there was once insulin coma, then ECT, then barbiturates, and finally chlorpromazine, there is now a huge range of treatments for the various psychiatric conditions. A whole new generation of major tranquillisers and anti-psychotic drugs have made the treatment of schizophrenia and psychosis much better and more tolerable. There is lithium for manic depression. And for anxiety and depression, the floodgates have opened, with Prozac and its successors being among the most widely prescribed drugs on the planet. Not all of these advances, however, have been entirely beneficial, as some of the drugs have been found to have some unwanted consequences. Barbiturates were widely prescribed as tranquillisers for mild anxiety, especially in the 1950s and '60s, until they found that some patients had become addicted to them. Then along came Valium, 'mother's little helper', which was supposed to be the wonder drug until it, too, was found to be addictive. A generation of Western housewives – because, by and large, the principal consumers of these drugs were the bored, stay-at-home wives – became addicted to prescription medicines. And there is evidence that the new generation of antidepressants may have some 'discontinuation problems' – that is, you feel funny when you stop taking them.

Aside from drugs and surgery, major advances were made in two other fields of interest to the person with Down's syndrome. The first was genetics, with the cause of Down's syndrome, an abnormal gene 21, being identified in 1959 by the French geneticist Jérôme Lejeune. The second was the development of antenatal screening, with ultrasound, blood tests and amniocentesis all being used to identify the abnormal foetus.

Despite all these advances, we are no nearer being able to cure Down's syndrome. But we are in a position to cure many of the abnormalities which shorten the life of the Down's syndrome patient, and treat some of the many complications of the condition. Gastrointestinal problems can be cured by surgery, as can heart defects. We can treat hypothyroidism with thyroxine. Depression, which is a major problem in Down's syndrome, and often previously undiagnosed, will respond to the new generation of antidepressants. We know a lot more about nutrition, so we can adjust the diet accordingly. Airway problems can be fixed with drugs and surgery. And, most importantly, we understand the need to work on physical conditioning, with physiotherapy, postural exercising and speech and language therapy.

All these advances mean that for the first time in human history, someone with Down's syndrome can anticipate a lifespan comparable with someone normally abled. It is not unusual for a person with Down's syndrome to live well into their fifties and sixties, compared with an average in the early twenties barely fifty years ago. This at first glance is a very positive achievement, a tribute to the efficacy of modern science. However, it has thrown up many difficulties, not the least of which is the moral argument about screening.

Antenatal screening for Down's syndrome began with a simple blood test which detected a rise in a substance called alpha-fetoprotein (AFP), an indicator of Down's syndrome. If the AFP came back raised, the woman was offered a termination. The problem with this test was that it was not infallible – like all screening tests – so some normal foetuses were terminated, while some Down's syndrome foetuses were missed. In both cases there were pretty devastating consequences for the mothers. Subsequently, the screening tests have become more sophisticated, with amniocentesis and chorionic villus sampling improving the identification rate, but there is still room for error. In 2006, 400 pregnancies were terminated after false positive results for Down's syndrome, which is a pretty horrifying number. It is a huge problem because at one point over 90 per cent of all Down's syndrome foetuses were terminated.

There are several issues arising from this. The first is the whole question of termination of pregnancy for medical reasons. As a doctor, who has seen the difficulties caused by trying to raise a disabled child, I believe this option has to be offered, and that the decision should be the parent's with support but not coercion from the medical profession one way or the other. (When I mentioned that I was writing this book to some former colleagues, and asked for their recollections of Down's syndrome families, one of the first words they used was 'divorce'.) The problem is that Down's syndrome is a condition of varying severity, and there is no way of knowing if the child you are aborting is seriously disabled or virtually normal. And then there is the changing outlook for a person with Down's syndrome. It is one thing offering a termination in the certain knowledge that you are sparing the child a life of misery, but when that child could enjoy a relatively normal life, where is the moral line? And moving on from that, there is also the question of whether you should perform surgery on seriously disabled infants with multiple birth defects. And we return to the heart of the matter which we touched on in Chapter 1 and which haunts our story – yes, people with Down's syndrome are different, but does that make them any less human than the rest of us?

I cannot pretend to know the answers, and I don't think that anybody does. To be honest, it is an uncomfortable subject to discuss because, as in so many areas of medical ethics, the options tend to be lose–lose. Unfortunately, the Down's syndrome story would not be complete without airing the moral and ethical dilemmas which face our society when dealing with issues like termination of pregnancy. You will get both sides of the argument today, and the debate is ongoing. Interestingly, it seems that women are increasingly choosing to progress with their pregnancies, so the numbers are falling.

To move on from medicine, the second great advance for people with Down's syndrome in the second half of the twentioeth century has been the development of specialist education. In the immediate post-war period, when learning difficulty patients were still in specialist units, a basic education was provided on site. As the old asylums closed, and people moved into specialist accommodation or stayed at home, the need for appropriate schooling became apparent. Initially, education authorities set up special needs schools to cater for the learning difficulty and other disabled communities, and many of these schools survive to this day. The educational establishment, however, became concerned at the isolating effect of these separatist establishments, and the often inappropriate selection of pupils. In the late 1980s the concept of 'special educational needs' took shape, embracing children with learning difficulty, disability and behavioural problems. The aim, which evolved over the next twenty years and is still evolving, was to get the child into an appropriate learning environment. This is not as easy as it sounds, which a variable condition like Down's syndrome neatly illustrates. A nearly normal Down's syndrome child could cope with a mainstream school, whereas one with severe developmental delay could not, so saying 'all Down's syndrome patients should be in a special school' is pointless. This would apply to all the other learning difficulty patients as well – they are all individuals, and need almost a bespoke solution to their needs.

The problem is that funding bespoke education for every child is expensive, so some form of grouping has to be considered. This is often complicated by the prevailing theory of the time, a phenomenon as prevalent in education as in any other profession. In the late 1980s and early 1990s, for example, there was a drive to shut down the special schools and shunt children into mainstream education. Part, at least, of the impetus for these changes came from the voluntary sector, like the Down's Syndrome Association. But, special school closure also angered some of the parents, and it led to some very determined campaigns to ensure that certain schools stayed open. So even within a particular special interest group you will find a range of opinions, an indication of how difficult it can be to get the balance right.

The world has moved on, and a greater understanding of the problem has seen a more diverse range of educational options for the Down's syndrome child. There are eight options currently available from state and charitable sources:

ordinary class
ordinary class with consultant

> ordinary class with itinerant special teacher
> ordinary class with withdrawal to a resource room
> special class plus part-time ordinary class
> full-time special class in ordinary school
> full-time special day school
> residential day school

Not all educational authorities would have all these options, but in most areas there should be a range of options to suit the individual child. More importantly, there are now services for pre-school children, where the family are visited by a home support teacher, where the process of assessing the individual child's educational needs is initiated. Educational authorities have special educational needs co-ordinators to plan care, and resources have been provided for specialist workers to go into schools. Research shows that Down's syndrome children educated in mainstream education, where appropriate, achieve better than those who are educated in specialist schools, so the aim is to get as many learning disability children into ordinary schools as possible. There is also a political and social agenda at work here, an attempt to integrate the disabled into normal society. Politicians, notably New Labour, have backed this drive with anti-discrimination legislation and more resources. Quite how it works in some of our schools I don't know, because the cruelty of children is frightening, but the theory is sound. It will probably take a generation to change attitudes.

Aside from this, the other great development in the education of learning difficulty patients has been the development of learning theory. Strangely enough, this has its origins in the work of Galton, of eugenics fame, and his early work on personality theory. This was developed and expanded by Jung, who recognised that different personality types took in information in different ways. A detailed explanation of the works of Jung is beyond the scope of this book, but to give two examples: a person with a preference for extroversion will learn by reacting with the external world, while the introverted personality will learn best by solitary study and reflection. Once you accept that this is the case, you can structure learning plans accordingly. And, again, once the ball is rolling, you can look for other clues to the individual's learning preference.

The interesting thing about this was the discovery that people with Down's syndrome tended to learn better visually than aurally, and sign language, both British sign language and a special one called Makaton, were used to facilitate learning for Down's syndrome children.

One of the reasons the end of the twentieth century saw such progress in the social and educational welfare of people with Down's syndrome was the rise of patient power, especially the power of their parents. In 1970 the Down's Syndrome Association was created in England, which rapidly became a powerful voice for Down's syndrome children and families. In the USA the National Assciation for Down Syndrome and the National Down Syndrome Society were formed in 1979. All these organisations provide support for people with Down's syndrome, generate and distribute information, organise local support groups, and fund research and awareness of the condition. The growth of the patient support group, of which these are prominent examples, has been one of the most effective therapeutic advances in the last fifty years. Many parents of Down's syndrome children go through a terrible time when the child is born. The literature resounds with horror stories of how they were told – often brusquely, with little empathy – and the list of potential problems. One father recalled:

> When my eldest, normal, son was born, nobody told me that he could get meningitis and be involved in an RTA. Yet he did both these things. When my daughter, who has Down's, was born, I received a litany of potential problems, from heart disease to infertility. Apart from the odd cold, she's fine.

In defence, it is only natural for the medical profession to think medically, and a disease name automatically triggers a cascade of information. And doctors are surprisingly unaware. I know my reaction, if I had to tell someone their child had Down's syndrome, would have been to pour out the list of potential ailments, and for most of my career I would have been completely unaware that maybe all of the things would not happen. The charities have provided a valuable resource for the medical profession, among other things.

But most importantly, they are a support for the family at its darkest hour. A common feeling described by new parents of a Down's syndrome child is the feeling that they are completely and utterly alone. And there is the shame, and feelings of inadequacy, and the minute dissection of all the things that happened during the pregnancy, and the guilt, and the blame, and all the rest of it. However well intentioned, the comforting hand on the shoulder and the 'It'll be all right, you'll see' coming from the doctor or family friend can be utterly meaningless. How would they know? If, however, that person has had a Down's syndrome child, their compassion is relevant, and, more importantly, their advice becomes something desperately important. A fellow parent of a child with Down's syndrome can tell you, 'Yes, you'll go through hell for the first six months but it will improve, and it may never be fine, but you'll cope', and you'll believe it. It sounds logical, getting fellow sufferers to help each other, but it has taken about two thousand years to sort out.

The following advances would not have been achieved without the lobbying of the Down's Syndrome Association: the 1981 Education Act, which gave parents the right to send their disabled children into mainstream schools; the provision of information to pregnant women about having a Down's syndrome baby; help for families to claim the appropriate benefits; education of the medical profession about Down's syndrome; and the ensuring that people with Down's syndrome get the necessary services from their community.

Aside from mainstream medicine and education, there are other communities and charities which provide care for people with Down's syndrome. There is the Down Syndrome Research Foundation, which looks for a cure for Down's syndrome, the Down's Heart Group, to help those with severe cardiac problems, Down

Syndrome Education International, and the Down Syndrome Training and Support Service, which helps people with Down's syndrome to find work. Other, broader-based charities like Mencap and MIND also provide services for people with Down's syndrome. And there are a host of others, both national and local, which provide a range of services for people with learning difficulties, including residential care.

One such organisation is Camphill, which provides residential sustainable communities based on the teachings of the anthroposophist Rudolf Steiner. Anthroposophy is a complex subject to explain, but essentially it believes that we are losing touch with our inner spiritual core, and so becoming disconnected from nature. Camphill communities seek to redress the balance with communal living, natural farming and natural medicine, among other things. Most importantly, for the person with Down's syndrome, they believe that each of us has a pure inner spiritual core unrelated to our external appearance. The Camphill communities were set up specifically to care for people with special needs, and for other mental illness. The first community was set up in 1939, in Scotland, and has spread to 22 countries. For much of its existence it has been regarded as wildly eccentric by mainstream education and medicine, but many of its values, – such as treating each person as a valued individual, the rejection of medication as the cure for all ills, and living a sustainable, holistic lifestyle – are now all mainstream ideals. Of course, not everybody could subscribe to the philosophy, but in the context of Down's syndrome they have an honourable record, and are an important part of the story.

The end of the twentieth century saw the advent of New Labour, and a blizzard of initiatives for health and social care. The most important was the setting of national standards of care, encompassed in the imposition of targets and the 'Quality and Outcomes Framework' which tied good practice into remuneration. For Down's syndrome patients there were new frameworks governing the relationship between patients, carers and service users, an updating of the Disability Discrimination Act, and changes to the benefit system to help disabled people. In practice this meant that the residential accommodation and care support had to reach certain standards, that the level of benefits was adequate, and, most importantly, that their disability should not be a bar to appropriate work.

So, in the space of less than fifty years, the situation for people with Down's syndrome has been transformed. They are no longer incarcerated in mental hospitals, facing a short and unproductive life surrounded by the rest of society's misfits. They are in the community, at home or in specialist accommodation. There are cures for their medical problems. Society is being educated to treat them as equals, backing this up with legislation where necessary. There is every prospect of some sort of meaningful work. The doors of the asylum have been opened, and although the world may not be quite as pleasant as it could have been, it was a whole lot better than what had gone before.

I think we should take a moment to reflect on this. All of us, and I am no exception, are guilty of believing sometimes that we live in miserable times, governed by a uniquely incompetent political class. And yet, all of us born and raised in the post-war world have lived in revolutionary times, at least as far as the treatment of the disabled is concerned. Since the Second World War our society has actively sought to improve the lives of the disabled through public money and legislation, and provided additional support through charitable giving and voluntary work. And although the driving force behind the Welfare State was Atlee's Labour Party, all the post-war governments have played their part in sustaining it, and helping some of the poorest and most vulnerable in society. We may find some of the hinterland around welfare unpalatable, and some of the political correctness risible, but the world for minorities like the disabled is a whole lot better now than fifty years ago, and we can all take pride in that achievement. And, most importantly, the impetus for nearly all of it has begun in Parliament.

So, far, though, we have been mainly talking about the position of people with Down's syndrome in society, and dealing with the psychiatric, social and political landscape of the person with learning difficulties. I think it's about time to stop dealing in abstracts and see what all these changes have meant for Down's syndrome people in our fast-moving and often confusing modern world.

6

A Day in the LIfe

The turn of the century, especially when it leads to a new millennium, is often seen as a time of profound change, and the dawn of the twenty-first century has been no exception. Within two years we had 9/11, and the start of a conflict between the Western world and radical Islam. We have been subjected to 'millennium' weather, with more natural disasters in the last few years than I can remember in the previous forty. We have had a crisis in the world's stockmarkets, the biggest for eighty years, which saw Britain 24 hours away from financial meltdown. In 2011, spontaneously, it seems, revolution spread through the Arab world, with governments overthrown in Tunisia and Egypt, and those in Libya and Syria fighting for their lives. Finally, as I write, the European Union, the great political invention of my lifetime, appears to be tottering as the people of Greece take to the streets. We are living, as the Chinese curse has it, in interesting times.

It is not all doom and gloom, however, because for some people in the West life has never been better. The child with Down's syndrome born in the UK today is joining a society that is one of the most advanced, certainly institutionally, in its attitude to the disabled. The reforms of the past fifty years have seen the creation of complex systems in health, education and community care, which have provided a network of support for the disabled and their families. As I will outline in the next chapter, there is still a long way to go to educate the public, but for the moment it is worth recording the successes.

It was only a hundred and fifty years ago that the syndrome was recognised, and in order to put the modern world in context it is worth reminding ourselves of the journey so far. At the time of Langdon Down, children with learning difficulties would be admitted to 'idiot' asylums, where, initially, they would receive special help with their disabilities. As the asylums became overcrowded, they were effectively just warehoused and left in institutions that were little better than prisons. Although reforms were implemented, and some places provided useful work and made attempts at education, the difficulties involved meant that little progress was made. Right up to the 1960s, the 'care pathway' for most Down's syndrome children was removal from the family and institutionalisation.

Then, slowly but surely, political legislation and medical advances meant that the purpose of the asylums was questioned, and community care became a reality. This in turn raised a whole new series of questions about care and education, and led to the creation of specialist residential homes and special schools.

As the process evolved, certain fundamental problems became apparent, the most notable of which was matching the degree of disability to the services required. The needs of a person with mild Down's syndrome were far different from the level of care and education required by someone who was severely disabled.

The need to place children in an appropriate environment saw the creation of the 'Statement of Educational Needs', an assessment of the individual child's ability. If a child was 'statemented' then the local education authority was required by law to provide extra educational input for that child. Although of great value in the vast majority of cases, it has become a controversial issue because of the financial and social aspects of the decision. As mentioned in the previous chapter, the cyclical nature of educational theory meant that boundaries between special schools and mainstream schools was forever shifting, which meant that borderline cases could find themselves in a special school one year and in a mainstream school the next.

Although the arguments are still raging, at the time of writing the situation is relatively stable. The 'Statement' has been refined over the years, so there are many fewer inappropriate placements. And outside of the educational system health and social services have developed care pathways to deal with the needs of people with learning disabilities. An extensive network now exists to ensure that people with Down's syndrome are recognised, and that they receive an appropriate level of education and care.

Once a child is born with Down's syndrome, health and social services are informed, and the needs of the family are assessed. The social services assessment will provide support, equipment and information about day care centres and respite care. Health visitors will monitor development, and the local surgery will deal with the medical needs, along with the paediatric department of the local hospital.

At a relatively early age, children will be assessed for learning disabilities, and a decision will be made about whether they can go through mainstream nursery and education, usually with additional help, or whether they need special schooling. The special educational needs assessment looks at the whole child rather than just the degree of formal learning difficulties, so the following are taken into account:

- the child's ability to perform routine educational tasks like reading, writing and arithmetic
- whether they can express themselves and understand what others are saying
- how they relate to adults
- whether they are behaving appropriately in a social and school setting
- their ability to organise themselves
- whether they have other needs, like sensory or physical problems which impair the child's ability to learn.

These are some of the criteria used to determine the educational future of the child. Many Down's syndrome children, and the majority of learning disability children, are now educated in mainstream schools with appropriate support. This can include extra teaching with one-to-one support, or, if the school is big enough, lessons with a class of fellow learning disability students. Being in a mainstream school is not without its share of problems, because although children with Down's syndrome can learn quickly, it may not be by formal teaching methods, and care must be taken to ensure that the children understand, rather than just mimic, what they are being told. Cruelty, persecution and a feeling that they are falling behind may send children with Down's syndrome into their shells. These disadvantages are balanced against the positive effect of being in a normal social environment, giving these children a chance to function independently in society. This is one of the problems faced by children raised in a closed environment, because by the time they reach adulthood they have become institutionalised and their chances of integration are much reduced.

Some children with Down's syndrome have severe learning disabilities, and for them a mainstream school is not an option. In England there is a network of special schools which cater for people with severe learning difficulties. I visited our local special school, the Heart of the Forest school in the Forest of Dean, to see for myself the problems faced by both the children and their carers.

The school takes children from as young as three, and may keep the children until they are nineteen. It is a day school, so the children are drawn from the local community. The school only takes children with learning disabilities, ranging from Down's syndrome, through autism and Asperger's syndrome, to cerebral palsy. It does not cater for physically disabled children.

All the children who enter the school are below level one on the educational scale, that is, the range of abilities you would expect from an average 5-year-old child. What this means in practice is that they struggle not only to learn to read and write, but also to

perform the basic functions of day-to-day life, like washing, dress-
ing and basic self-care. All of the children had difficulty communi-
cating with the outside world. It is the task of the Heart of the
Forest, in partnership with the parents, to maximise the abilities of
the individual child, and as well as trying to teach the children
formal educational skills, the staff also have to work on some of the
behavioural problems unique to this group of children. My first
impression was that not only did you need the patience of a saint,
but the ability to concentrate under conditions which would have
the rest of us climbing up the walls. Allied to this, one needed an
almost military sense of discipline to ensure that the care pathway
for the individual child was administered at all times, something
which may sound a bit odd but will become self-evident as we go
along.

To give an idea of the problems posed by people with severe
learning difficulties, it is worth reminding ourselves how a normally
abled child learns. Beginning with objects, children quickly learn
the names of things, and their function – for example, they learn
the word 'cup' and rapidly associate this with a drink. They learn to
control a pen to write the alphabet, and identify groups of letters
as words. They then learn to match the words on the page with
objects in real life. And, most importantly, they can communicate
their understanding, usually verbally.

Once the basics have been mastered, more complicated educational tasks can be attempted – arithmetic, sentence construction,
painting, drawing and storytelling. The children learn to memorise
consciously as well as unconsciously, and as a consequence of all
these developments acquire a significant breadth of knowledge
and skills in a short space of time. As well as educational development, children learn social skills, like self-care, how to behave, how
to react with classmates, and how to interact with adults. By the
time children leave primary education they are formed, independent people, although lacking physical and emotional maturity.

People with profound learning disability, and Down's syndrome
in particular, can have problems at every stage of this process.

To go through it stage by stage, at the most basic level they may have visual or hearing impairment, so they may struggle to take in information. Even if the information is retained, it is not processed in the same way as a normally abled child, either not being recognised or being processed but over a much longer time span. For example, a severely disabled child with Down's syndrome may never make the connection between 'cup' and 'drink', and therefore require someone to hold the cup up for him or her. That would be rare, a more likely scenario being that the connection is made, but over a much longer period of time, say months or even years, and only after intensive input from parents and carers. And that may go for every single action that we take for granted, like hanging up a coat, or holding a fork. Poor physical co-ordination may make writing difficult, a skill some may not master. Again, we return to the idea that the brain in Down's syndrome is missing vital connections, which can only be corrected, if at all, by intensive external input and repetitive training.

Finally, there is the difficulty that people with Down's syndrome have in communication, either because their neural pathways are not developed,or because of physical problems with the tongue and limb movements. This is an extremely common problem with many types of learning disability, and the most challenging to understand and treat. And it must be the most frustrating for the sufferer – imagine trying to get through a day without being able to articulate words properly, or even write them down. You would be helpless, wouldn't you? (In the interests of research, I tried this. Without a support network, I didn't last an hour, and, yes, I was helpless.)

However, if you are so disabled, and there is no other option, what are you going to do? One interesting result of the development of specialist schooling has been the recognition that people with severe learning disabilities are constantly trying to communicate, but they are using other means which we do not recognise as communication. For example, children may use certain hand movements to indicate their wants, or swaying, or banging the table, or even just using facial expressions. Once a means of communication has been identified, then it can be worked on. Sign language is very popular in special schools – standard sign language, Makaton (a special form of signing especially useful for the disabled) and a simpler form called Signalong. Children with Down's syndrome are very quick to pick up sign language, in some cases faster than their carers.

Each child in the school had a 'communication passport', a single sheet of laminated A4 which detailed their personal history, what they like and dislike, and, crucially, their favoured method of communication. The importance of this document in facilitating continuity of care cannot be overemphasised. One of the problems with learning disability is retention of skills, and a new carer or teacher who is unaware of the child's communication preferences may undo some of the work that has gone before. Repetition and constant encouragement are the keystones of education in special schools.

It is not, however, as straightforward as all that. Each child is an individual and will learn at their own rate, acquiring a mixed bag of skills. They are also children, and are just as prone to being lazy or naughty as other children. For example, one has to be very careful about using commands, as it may stop the child from learning for itself. If you tell a child to 'hang your coat up', and the child obeys, that would appear to be a success. However, you may reach the situation where the child only hangs their coat up in response to a verbal prompt, and then has to be re-educated to go to the coat rack on entering the room. This would be done by leading the child over to the rack and demonstrating, wordlessly, that they must hang their coat up.

In the learning disability classroom, there are a wide variety of communication aids, including picture/sound toys, tapes and interactive displays. Every possible means of communication is explored, and learning will, within certain frameworks, be tailored to the individual child. There is also, within the school, speech therapy and occupational therapy, a gym, a 'sensory room' where the student's senses, like touch, are stimulated, and there is a pool for hydrotherapy.

Teaching people with severe learning difficulties is therefore an art, and relies on a holistic approach to the individual's capabilities, with the acknowledgement that each child may attain a different educational level. It is, though, still a school, with a structured approach to the child's education, so there is a learning disability curriculum. Trying to teach English and Maths in formal lessons is obviously difficult, so staff begin by using interesting subjects to introduce other concepts. When I was there the 3–5-year-olds were doing 'Under the Sea', and were painting fish (real fish, trout as it happens, which I thought was very brave). So from that you get colours, names, numbers (although that was too advanced for that class), tactile awareness and co-ordination. Examples of the children's creative work were all over the school.

Both Maths and English received special attention. The school had a special system, numicon, which uses coloured pegs on a board and coloured shapes – three is I-shaped, four a square, and so on – to approach the subject of addition. Again, I was struck by the slightly tangential approach to familiar subjects, very different for those of us brought up with a different system.

The endless patience displayed by the staff in their handling of formal education was matched by their discipline in forming the social skills of the children. Children with Down's syndrome are particularly prone to performing, which can be cute when they are young but quite inappropriate when carried into adult life. One of the teachers told me of a young girl who would hit her mother's behind, laugh and say 'fat bottom!' – very funny at home but not the sort of thing it is advisable to try in the supermarket queue. This was often one of the most difficult things to correct, as parents and children failed to see the behaviour as a problem, often, from the best of motives, encouraging the child to seek attention.

The children were assessed every year, and their progress meticulously charted. As many are below the level of key stage 1, a system called P scales has been developed to record the individual child's development. This encompasses all aspects of the child's educational and social abilities with categories like 'can hold a cup', 'drinks from a cup', 'uses fork', 'recognises words', building up a comprehensive picture of the child and their progress through the school. Those of us in the public services often rail against the profusion of bureaucracy, but occasionally it performs a vital service, as with these children.

Using these recording tools, and looking at the quality of the work displayed, it was apparent that the older children had made considerable progress while they were at the school. As well as more formal educational subjects, they were taught life skills like nutrition, cooking and shopping to prepare them for life after school. And when it was time to leave, the school liaised with appropriate agencies to ensure the children were placed appropriately.

Much of this will sound mundane to the general reader, but it is the focus on the mundane which has led to the improvement in care for people with Down's syndrome. Before we had special schools, and a learning disability curriculum, people with moderate to severe Down's syndrome would have spent their childhood in an asylum or residential home, and be almost as dependent at eighteen as they were at eight. Now, if the child with Down's syndrome has the ability to learn a skill, like writing, or maths, or cooking, then that skill will be developed to the maximum, meaning that the future adult may be able to self-care, or live independently from their parents, or even have their own life within a secure framework. These are tangible and cost-effective achievements.

What impressed me most about the school, however, was its ethos, and the atmosphere generated by the lovely modern buildings and, most importantly, the dedicated staff. In a world which is often brash and coarse, it is rare to find a place wholly dedicated to improving the lives of people less fortunate than ourselves. It was the sort of place where one could tell that the staff were motivated by their own personal standards, rather than by diktat from above, which is the best guarantee of high-quality care. The story of Down's syndrome down the years is pretty grim, but the school was a shining example of how the future could be brighter.

There is, of course, another side to the educational system, and that is the role played by parents. As I mentioned in Chapter 1, probably the most challenging thing about being the parent of a child with Down's syndrome is the sheer volume of extra tasks you are required to perform. One of the best accounts of raising a child with Down's syndrome is *Helen, The Light, Our Light* by Angela Zueger-Caplan. It tells the story of her daughter Helen, from birth to age 11, and is illustrated throughout with reproductions of Helen's actual developmental and school reports, which makes the book a unique record of Down's syndrome. Helen has the form of Down's syndrome known as 'mosaic', which means that her cells are not uniformly affected by the condition. As a result, people with mosaic Down's syndrome tend to be at the high end of the performance scale. They account for only a tiny minority – about one per cent – of Down's syndrome cases.

Helen was born in 1976, so some of the education theory and practice is out of date, but the general principles, and the interaction between the child and the family and the medical and educational establishment, remain true to this day. The book is well written, and Angela Zueger-Caplan has that rare gift, an ability to see both sides of the question, even when her own behaviour is under scrutiny. The result is a detailed and engrossing read. Helen comes across as stubborn, entertaining and something of an attention-seeker, but with great abilities and an engaging personality. She has a normally abled brother, Phillip, and the book highlights the contrast between the development of the 'normal' child and the developmental delay of a child with Down's syndrome. The family were greatly helped by an educational psychologist, Dr Rex Brinkworth, who had devised schedules designed to accelerate the development of the learning disability child. Dr Brinkworth was acknowledged in the 1980s as a pioneer in the field of therapy for Down's syndrome, and he helped to found the Down's Syndrome Association.

The book also shows how the personalities of teachers can affect progress, as children with Down's syndrome can be more sensitive than most to perceived rudeness or rejection. In the course of their story, the Zueglers come across all sorts of people, from those with genuine skill and compassion to people whose crass insensitivity makes them unfit for the caring professions, a surprisingly common finding in accounts of the condition.

The book illustrates the dynamic that exists between the child with Down's syndrome, the parent, and the educational system, and the complexities of those relationships. The detailed descriptions of consultations with professionals and the inclusion of Helen's actual reports bring her to life, and set her in the context of a world we can all understand. It is a valuable resource for anyone who has a child with Down's syndrome, but I would also recommend it to a wider readership, and anyone who is interested in the plight of people with learning disability.

When a child leaves special school, they come under the care of the Community Learning Disabilities Team, or CLDT as it is more commonly known. The team comprises occupational therapists, learning disability nurses, and speech therapists, with input from a consultant psychiatrist with an interest in learning difficulties. The teams are organised around the areas covered by each district council, so in Gloucestershire we have a Forest CLDT, a Gloucester CLDT, a Cotswold CLDT and so on. The teams cover all learning disability patients in the community, both in residential homes and those still at home. It is their task to ensure that learning disability patients are identified, and that they receive the appropriate level of care and support. This may sound unremarkable, but in fact it is a terrific advance on what happened even thirty years ago. When I started as a GP back in the early 1980s, it was not unusual to come across families with disabled children living in poverty and squalor, who had not seen a doctor for years. Apart from their health problems, there was little else you could do for them, and there was not the advanced system of social services that exists today. Similar families these days are much better cared for by the state, and again, we should be proud of this. It is such a shame that the disabled are still hidden away, because if people could see what a difference the money made then 'national insurance' or 'community charge' would cease to be abstract concepts but something with tangible value.

On a practical level, the structure of community learning diffi- culty teams means that the individual client gets a properly assessed and appropriate level of care. Whereas earlier, occupa- tional therapy, speech therapy,and nursing input all needed sepa- rate referrals, now a single phone call is often all that is needed. And the creation of specialist teams means that they rapidly gain more expertise than individual medical practitioners, so their recommendations carry more weight. Not that all GPs see it quite like this, of course, but the 'creative tension' in community services would take another book to explain.

One of the biggest challenges faced by the team was by the speech and language therapist. Although I was aware that com- munication is a problem, I did not realise the sheer numbers involved. Over 80 per cent of people with learning difficulties have a communication problem, and 50 per cent have significant difficulties. These include:

- understanding speech, writing and symbols
- having a sufficient vocabulary to express themselves
- being able to construct a sentence
- maintaining focus and concentration
- fluency, for example stammering
- poor social skills, inhibiting appropriate communication
- physical problems, like tongue deformities in Down's syn- drome.

If the aim of therapy is to get people with Down's syndrome to integrate into normal society, one can see the scale of the problem. And people with learning difficulty are vulnerable, more likely to be victims of crime or physical and sexual abuse. They are also likely to exhibit some challenging behaviour themselves, either prone to violent outbursts or inappropriate sexual behaviour. The CLDT team often walks the high wire.

Quite apart from providing better services, the CLDT is actively screening people with Down's syndrome for signs of Alzheimer's and dementia. Alzheimer's disease is more common in people with

Down's syndrome, and it not only strikes earlier, when people are in their fifties, but also progresses faster. This is important because the neurodegenerative diseases like motor neurone disease, Parkinson's, multiple sclerosis and Alzheimer's are one of the last group of diseases with no meaningful cure, and the focus has to be on supportive care.

All people with Down's syndrome in the Forest are automatically screened for Alzheimer's at age 35, but patients can be referred into the screening process at any point if carers or staff are concerned. The purpose of the screening is to alert medical and social care, and put in place measures to deal with the problem.

Again, this may sound routine, boring even. From a practical and financial point of view, however, it is a huge advance on the old-fashioned laissez-faire approach of days gone by. What used to happen – and this goes for a lot of illness, not just Alzheimer's – is that the person with Down's syndrome living with their parents would, over a period of years, slowly go downhill, the burden of caring for them getting imperceptibly heavier. As this happens, tension mounts as the carer gets swamped with more and more tasks, until one day the tipping point is reached, all the frustration and anger spills out, and the situation descends into chaos. (Most GPs of my vintage would tell you that this inevitably occurred at 11 o'clock on a Friday night.) And then you would have the awful job of sorting out the mess, which almost always involved hospital admission. Then there would be the task of finding community care (of course there would be none available for six months), and dealing with relatives demanding to know why nothing had been done ... it was always a nightmare. The current situation is infinitely better.

There are many reasons for the improvement, but the main ones are modern society's ability to change its preconceptions and learn from previous experiences. If that sounds self-evident, remember that it was only fifty years ago that the medical profession seriously believed that people with Down's syndrome had a fixed disability which was incapable of improvement. The idea of 'best practice' and evidence-based medicine, where treatments and therapies are dispassionately evaluated and condensed into workable guidelines has revolutionised the practice of medicine and social care. As far as caring for people with Down's syndrome is concerned, this has reflected the findings of special schools, that it is vitally important to work on communication, that children with Down's syndrome may need intensive interaction to improve, and that one must always be on the lookout for challenging or inappropriate behaviour. The importance of being in a calm environment, particularly as they get older and could be developing Alzheimer's, is vital, as is the attitude of their carers. One of the mantras of the new care approach states that '90 per cent of catastrophic behaviour in people with dementia is induced by carers and the environment'. More people with Down's syndrome get into trouble through being in the wrong place, or with overworked carers, than through their own actions.

As well as Alzheimer's, people with Down's syndrome can develop physical disease as they age, notably epilepsy and thyroid disease, and the screening process keeps an eye out for these as well.

The other important difference in the modern management of Down's syndrome is the involvement of multiple agencies in case management. Although sometimes this can result in confusion and, occasionally, disaster, it has the beneficial effect of bringing different abilities to the table, and ensures that nothing is overlooked. A person with Down's syndrome looked after by a single health professional – as used to happen in the days of single-handed GPs – is entirely reliant on that person's knowledge and experience, which may or may not be adequate. In the modern world that is unacceptable, although I should point out that there are significant advantages to having your health looked after by a single doctor, not the least of which is continuity of care. But this is another argument for another time.

The involvement of multiple agencies should, in theory, ensure that no one with Down's syndrome or learning disability should languish unrecognised in the community. However, as the CLDT team told me, this is not necessarily the case in practice. Anyone who is born in an NHS hospital, or is registered in an NHS practice, should be picked up. There are, though, all sorts of people and organisations who operate outside of society's formal structures. Most counties have a traveller population, who may or may not remain in one place for months, and who certainly may not register with a local practice. Some immigrant communities where English is not the first language may shelter disabled people. Charities and trusts with residential homes may have a shifting population, and could harbour people with Down's syndrome. Fortunately, the numbers involved in these circumstances are likely to be small.

The need to know how many people have Down's syndrome in the community, and the severity of their condition, may sound a little sinister, especially to those of us who are worried about the cavalier attitude of the modern world to personal information. In a medical situation, however, it is much better to know that things are going downhill well in advance, because plans can be made and the fallout from the problem minimised. What everyone dreads is the unknown patient with severe disabilities who is suddenly presented to the services with a plea that 'something must be done, we can't cope any more'. Such situations are stressful, take time, divert attention away from other patients, are expensive to resolve, and usually generate more long-term problems than they solve. So, for people with Down's syndrome who are requiring care, 'the price of safety is eternal vigilance'.

One final note is a plea from the public services involved in the care of people with learning difficulties. Although the reforms have been, by and large, a benefit, many frontline workers are beginning to suffer from organisational fatigue, and are beginning to resent the endless 'change agenda' which has come to dominate the public services. The following quote used to be pinned up in our health centre:

> We trained hard ... but it seemed that every time we were beginning to form up into teams we would be reorganised. I was to learn later in life that we tended to meet any new

situation by reorganising; and a wonderful method it can be for creating the illusion of progress while producing confusion, inefficiency, and demoralisation.

It is, wrongly, attributed to Petronius Arbiter, a Roman author of the first century, but it was probably invented in the USA in the late 1950s. Although we have had some great reforming governments since the war, we have also wasted billions of pounds on untried, slightly bizarre organisational theories, which seem to be intent on denuding the front line of competent staff. But, it was probably always the same, and I have no doubt it is the same in the private sector as well. *Plus ca change* ...

Lastly, we come to the issue of accommodation, and as far as residential accommodation goes, there is a mixed provision. The range of community services means that most children live at home, with varying degrees of support. For some children and families this is not appropriate, so there are a number of residential special schools scattered throughout the country. This is not preventing organisations from looking at more innovative ways to deliver care to people with learning disabilities. Providers of residential care are moving away from the old concept of 'one size fits all' to more radical concepts of accommodation for people with learning difficulties. Of course, many severely disabled people need 24-hour institutional care, but the momentum is shifting towards making learning disability patients as independent as possible. Different forms of accommodation are being explored, such as purpose-built accommodation and flats. It is a long way from the asylum.

This process has been facilitated by changes in the structure of the NHS, and in particular the creation of Primary Care Trusts between 2000 and 2010. Although as a GP I would have issues with them, there is no doubt that they encouraged creative thinking, and in particular the need to look outside traditional structures for solutions, and to work in partnership with other organisations. The result, in Gloucestershire, is that residential care for learning disability patients in Gloucestershire is provided not by the NHS or the local authority, but by a charity called the Brandon Trust. This organisation has a proven track record in providing care for people with learning difficulties, and won the contract to become the 'preferred provider' for Gloucestershire. Getting the NHS to change is like turning a super tanker, whereas smaller units are more flexible, and as long as the licensing and monitoring systems for these organisations is robust, then they are the way forward.

It has also been recognised, and this is often very difficult for parents, that teenagers with Down's syndrome need their independence, just like anyone else, and that there comes a time for them to leave home. If you have given up a sizeable chunk of your life to bringing up someone who still needs care, it must be very difficult to let go. But, as all of us who have children realise, not only do the children need to leave to develop as adults, we need them to leave as well. There is some kind of unwritten law that means that being at home after a certain age is unhealthy for both parties, and some people with Down's syndrome are no different in this respect.

And that, in a nutshell, is where we are in 2012. I am sure that if Langdon Down could return and see all that has been accomplished, he would approve wholeheartedly. What would have amazed him is what is to come next, the emergence of people with Down's syndrome and their families into the public consciousness through the media. And not necessarily as nice little mawkish cutie-pies either, but as complex, and sometimes angry, individuals who have grown tired of being patronised. The world of the disabled is becoming radicalised.

7

The Twenty-First Century and Beyond

As we reflect on the story of Down's syndrome it is probably true to say that medical and social advances have occurred so rapidly in the last sixty years that it is impossible to select one and say 'this was the most important single development in the history of Down's syndrome'.

There is one event, however, which was totally unique – the publication, in 1967, of *The World of Nigel Hunt: The Diary of a Mongoloid Youth*. This was the first book published by a person with Down's syndrome, and the first appearance of someone with learning disabilities in the mainstream media. The book is an account by Nigel of some of the events in his life, written in the diary style, from which he emerges as a complex individual very far removed from the image traditionally enjoyed by 'mongols' (I apologise for using the term, but it is the word used throughout the book). It was a revolutionary event because, with one bound, the traditional concept of people with learning disability as 'unimprovable idiots' was dispelled.

The book is a fascinating study, both of Nigel and the way he thinks, and attitudes towards the disabled in the 1960s. The Preface is written by his father, Douglas, who sets the story in context, and provides a few helpful annotations along the way. Perhaps the most telling comment comes when Nigel is about five, and his parents are summoned to see the county mental health officer. Here is the story in Douglas Hunt's own words: 'The first thing the good lady said to us – in Nigel's hearing, of course – was "Oh, yes, a little mongoloid. Quite uneducable. Do you want him put away?" '

Nigel's parents refused the offer of 'putting him away', preferring instead to pour their heart and soul into seeing if he could be educated. His mother, in particular, spent hours with him, and almost single-handedly taught him to read. It was not easy, however, as Douglas Hunt records: 'One must not only have unbounded patience and a single-minded devotion to the task in hand; one must also have faith that the goal will be reached.' In the case of the Hunt family, that goal was reached.

Trying to convince Nigel's teachers that this was the case proved a little more difficult. The mantra of the time was that 'people with Down's syndrome cannot read', and when Douglas Hunt demonstrated that Nigel could read, one of his headmasters shrugged and said, 'Yes, but he doesn't understand.' Douglas Hunt replied by asking, 'When you give him a note with an instruction on it does he comply?', to which the teacher could only look shamefaced. Nigel also learnt to type by watching his father, another skill thought to be beyond the reach of people with Down's syndrome. They took Nigel to see a Professor Penrose, at the time the leading authority in learning disability research, who initially refused to believe that Nigel could both read and type. He rapidly changed his mind after witnessing Nigel in action, and he became a great supporter of the family, writing the Foreword to the book, and praising it as an essay of 'considerable scientific interest'.

The story of how his mother taught him to read is fascinating. She realised instinctively that Nigel was not making progress through the 'look and read' method, so she started to spell short words to him phonetically, using household items. For example, the washing powder 'Daz' became 'Der, Ah, Zer', and the change in emphasis saw Nigel make rapid progress. One morning his mother found him in the kitchen going through the cupboards and heard him reading labels on the tins. From there it was natural to give him a book to read, which he managed first time, and with very little hesitation. All the time and effort expended by Nigel, and Grace, his mother, had been rewarded. Douglas Hunt makes the important point that the speed with which he read meant that Nigel knew a lot more than he let on, a characteristic of Down's syndrome people in general. Douglas and Grace Hunt were often surprised by Nigel's sudden mastery of a new task, although they both recognised that Nigel was extremely reluctant to demonstrate his abilities until he had perfected them.

It was not, however, all plain sailing. Nigel initially had a filthy temper, which made the task of educating him difficult, and it was only the saintly patience and firm handling of his mother which cured him of this trait. And encouraging his abilities made him more independent, which was a bit of a two-edged sword for the family. One morning he woke early and heard on the radio that it was the day of the Trooping of the Colour. Nigel decided to go to London to watch it, without, unfortunately, telling his parents. After 'a lovely day' he realised he had no money to get home, so, he said,

> I phoned my father to tell him I had no money to come home with. With that remark my father couldn't get through to me, the operator said to my father, 'You can reverse the charges and can talk to him as long as you like.' After a while my father phoned Scotland Yard to come and pick me up and a policeman came for me. I was at the police station drinking orange juice when my father found me. He said 'fancy you going to town so early', and so he found me. Then came lunch time. I had to wait till I got home. When I got home I had lunch and I enjoyed it very much. My father got cross because he had missed a day's shopping.

Missed a day's shopping! His parents were sick with anxiety. Nigel had simply got up, taken nine pence (old pence, 3.75 pence in today's money, although probably worth about £5 now) from his moneybox, walked to the station and caught a train to London (they lived in the London suburbs, in Pinner). In many ways this is a classic illustration of the challenges facing the carers of people with slight to moderate Down's syndrome. Nigel was able to plan the trip, get some money, buy a ticket from the station, navigate through London, and watch the Trooping of the Colour. Unfortunately, he did not tell his parents, had insufficient money for the train home, and was then effectively stranded. This was an expedition that could have easily ended in disaster. Fortunately he had the good sense to phone his parents, and one can only imagine their feelings when he was finally located. Relief alternating with blind fury, I should imagine.

What it illustrates is the patchwork nature of the intellectual capabilities of people with Down's syndrome, as if some parts of the brain are working normally, while others are silent. There is the ability to plan to achieve a goal, but no thought given to the potential problems in embarking on such a course of action, or the impact of the action on other people. Why did he leave without telling his parents? And why did he only take nine pence? What about food? And, what would happen if he couldn't get home? None of these things had been thought through.

If you look at the way Nigel writes – and he was 17 when he began the book – his style is a curious mix of the adult and the child, leaning heavily on the latter. Here is his account of a visit to one of his aunts, Auntie Mabs:

> I stalked in and had a bit of a talk and I said, 'I wonder if I can hear some records'. She said, 'Yes, do.' Then I would play them one at a time and I announce them. I said, 'Here is the Beatles singing "A Hard Day's Night" ', and, baton poised, I conducted them through. One day there was a knock at the door, and in walked Bruce, one of my auntie's friends, and I played 'Love Me Tender' sung by Richard Chamberlain, better known as the B.B.C.'s Dr Kildare, and Bruce danced with Auntie Mabs.

Once the twins (his aunts) or two, mind, took us to see my friend Yvonne at Croydon, and coming back from her place was like hell, we were lost in Hyde Park and there we were sitting like three Charlie's singing 'All Through The Night' and it was midnight when we got back and Dad was having his night's sleep. [His father added this rider: *Actually Dad was not, the silly fool was worrying himself sick as usual.*]

You see what I mean? There is something not quite right about it, not fully adult nor mainly childlike, but odd, as if Nigel is coming at life from a completely different angle. The key to unlocking Down's syndrome probably lies in understanding that thought process.

Finally, in case you think that looking after Nigel was an unremitting horror story, let me quote his father's Foreword:

This is Nigel's book, his own autobiography, and ... I must let him tell his own story. However, I feel that we, his parents, owe a few more words of encouragement to those who face the same problems we have had.

'Problem' is the word, not 'tragedy'.

Nigel has brought us untold joy. He has been loving, considerate, generous, and immensely rewarding. In many ways we have faced far fewer problems than do most parents of modern teenagers. In many ways he is far more capable of looking after himself. And he has started his first book at the age of seventeen ... Nigel is not a genius, though he may be a genius manqué ... But he is learning. This, above all, is the message we, his parents, would like to give to our readers. PEOPLE WITH DOWN SYNDROME CAN LEARN AND GO ON LEARNING IF THEY ARE GIVEN THE ENCOURAGEMENT.

They are children like any others, and like any others are both a blessing and a discipline. The parents of mongoloids have different problems from those of other parents; they miss some of the joys that other parents have, but they also have joys unknown to the parents of normal children.

Without being pompous or over-pious, I think we can both truly say that we accepted Nigel as a gift from God which we were greatly honoured to receive. He is an individual soul, as precious as any other, and we deemed it a great privilege that we were entrusted with this precious soul in a somewhat handicapped body, who needed especial care and understanding. We would not exchange him for the most brilliant child in the world and we have been richly and abundantly rewarded for all that we have tried to do for him.

The book threw open the musty curtains and allowed light into the world of learning disabilities. Although there has not been a flood of people with Down's syndrome into the public consciousness, they have a presence in the media that was unknown before the 1960s. Since the publication of Nigel Hunt's book, people with Down's syndrome, and their families, have been encouraged to share their experiences in print. The result is nearly a thousand books on the subject, covering all aspects of Down's syndrome, from the medical facts to first-person accounts of living with the syndrome.

Perhaps the most compelling are the stories of the parents, or, more particularly, the mothers. The confessional aspect of modern life is not to everyone's taste, but in the case of Down's syndrome it has provided a valuable resource for parents and carers of learning disability children. One such book is *Gifts*, the personal stories of mothers of Down's syndrome children in North America. Some of the mothers knew they were carrying a Down's syndrome child because of screening, others only found out at birth. Their stories are revealing, because they have a pattern.

The first emotion experienced by parents when they are informed is, unsurprisingly, a visceral shock which shakes them both to the core. This was almost universal, however otherwise hard-headed and resourceful the parents believed themselves to be. This was followed by a difficult period, which probably only the individual can fully describe, where a variety of emotions – bitterness, disappointment, hatred, fear, inadequacy, determination, optimism and love – slew around in an agitated mind. This is almost always described as the most challenging time for the mother, and puts the family under enormous strain. Some mothers cannot face taking their baby home, and reject it completely, giving it up for adoption. It is a common time for partnerships to break up, especially if the father is unable to cope with a disabled child. Particularly hard hit are those families who have tried to plan the perfect life, some mothers finding it very difficult to switch off the cycle of blame and self recrimination. If they get through it, paradoxically, they can often become the most staunch advocates for their children.

Then, slowly for some but more usually quite rapidly, the doubts and fears get swept away to be replaced by pride and love. I apologise if this sounds a little mawkish, but it is the only way I can describe the most commonly expressed event in the stories of these mothers. Just like Douglas Hunt, they become aware that their child is unique, and although he or she is not 'normal' they are special. None of the stories in the book was along the lines of 'My child has Down's syndrome but we're going to make the best of it'; virtually all of them were 'My child happens to have Down's syndrome, life goes on as normal'. This is not to say that they didn't acknowledge the difficulties, but, like the Hunt family, they realised that whatever their children lacked, they made up for in other ways. Often the tipping point for families was the presence of other siblings, whose unquestioning acceptance of their brother or sister with Down's syndrome swept away many of the doubts and fears.

Although some of the accounts can be over-sentimental, most are not, being quite candid about the positive and negative qualities of their children. The children that emerge from these accounts are just like other children in their range of characteristics. Probably the one area where children with Down's syndrome may differ is in the adolescent years, being less prone to the temptations and pitfalls of that most trying of times. This is one area which is dependent on the degree of disability, and the degree of care the individual requires. If the person with Down's syndrome requires residential or institutional care, and has severe learning difficulties, then their ability to form relationships is clearly compromised. Other than that, though, it is business as usual.

One thing which surprised me was how the major initial worry of many parents, the degree of care the individual required, seemed to fade into the background. Very few mentioned the number of extra tasks involved in the care of their child with Down's syndrome, almost as if it rapidly became routine. The main exception to this rule were the mothers who were single parents and back at work, and they often told of the fight they had to get proper facilities for their children. On both sides of the Atlantic, one of the main driving forces for change in the care of learning disabilities has been parent power.

It is not easy. The stories are littered with examples of the children becoming seriously ill, with anything from heart disease to cancer. One woman, Ann Bremer, whose son developed leukaemia, likened him to the Dean of a College, in that through him she learnt many things, which she likened to classes. So she had Class 105 – Health, Class 201 – Acronyms, Class 101 – Appearances, and so on. The one I particularly liked was Class 301 – Dealing with the Uninformed, or How and When to Educate Jerks. All the tales have encounters with people who are particularly insensitive, often made harder by the fact that they may be family or close friends. This is one area where the general public could improve dramatically, the way we react to people with learning difficulties.

The central theme of the stories, however, is the way in which all these mothers felt that their lives had been enriched. Echoing Douglas Hunt's words, they felt that caring for a child with Down's syndrome had been a privilege. I particularly liked the story of one woman whose life was otherwise perfect – loving husband, nice house, good jobs, holiday home, fit and healthy – and for whom the diagnosis of Down's syndrome was initially devastating. Her child was now grown up and, looking back, she thought that she had been lucky (and I paraphrase): 'My life would have been boring. I would have been like everyone else, back at work, children with nanny, onward and upward. Instead I had to deal with this problem, and I found out things about myself which I never knew. I had to do things which I would not have dreamed of in a million years, and I'm glad I did. Looking back my life was so shallow, and it would have continued that way. It made me a better person.'

The final thing, which nearly all the contributors relate, is the special nature of the relationship with their child with Down's syndrome. One of the common misconceptions about people with Down's syndrome is that they are universally 'gentle, cheerful, and the most amiable of learning disability people', as one academic put it, and this leads to the other delusion that the family relationship is one of gooey sentimentality. This is completely wrong. There are the usual family fights, tantrums, good times and bad times, which you get in any other family, with one exception. The particular nature of Down's syndrome, which requires more care on the part of the parent in some areas and less anxiety in others, does make for a different relationship. This is not to say that it is deeper or more affectionate than parents' relationships with normally abled children, just different. That is about as near as I can get to describing it.

Closer to home, the British journalists Dominic Lawson and Simon Barnes have both written movingly about their children who have Down's syndrome. Dominic Lawson has written a particularly interesting piece about the issues around termination, and the dangers of a return to eugenics. The medical profession does not come out of this well, it has to be said, seeming to be overwhelmingly pro-termination, and often curt and dismissive in manner. One of the justifications for termination used is the economic argument, which goes, 'Down's syndrome pregnancies should be terminated because the children will cost so much to look after'. This is an argument which is increasingly applied to all minorities who might require treatment, like smokers, the elderly, heavy drinkers, and the like. One of the most subtle pieces of political manipulation in modern times has seen this attitude become, almost, government policy, with hardly any form of reasoned discussion at all. As Dominic Lawson points out, how can we judge the quality of life of someone with Down's syndrome? And yet we are moving ever closer to a world where money is the only thing that matters. If anyone were to ask me the biggest single change in healthcare in my lifetime, I would say that 'cash' has replaced 'care' as the watchword for the New NHS. It has also lifted up a flat stone and given free rein to every medical and political control freak in the country, and, believe me, there are plenty of those. One of the founding principles of the NHS is that people who are ill require care, full stop, regardless of how they have come by their illness, and if we are going to change it then let's have the debate in plain view, not stitched up behind closed doors by the great and good. Anyway, rant over.

The children with Down's syndrome discussed in *Gifts*, these articles, and the many other accounts on the shelves, are the lucky ones, coming from largely stable, well-motivated backgrounds. There is a dark side, however, one which surfaces occasionally, but is largely hidden. The bad and abusive parents don't tend to write motivational books, their actions only coming to light in the social services departments across the country. Children with Down's syndrome are as likely to be in families with alcohol or drug problems as any other, and if they happen to live in the wrong part of town then just going outside the door could be a problem. The suicide of the Pilkington family, mother and disabled daughter, came after years of persecution from local people, and the litera-ture resounds with stories of disabled people persecuted by their communities. And it is sometimes no better in residential care, where even the profusion of guidelines and the most exhaustive inspection system in living memory is unable to stop the abuse of the disabled. At the time of writing, a learning disability home in Bristol has just been exposed on the *Panorama* programme, with disturbing pictures of people with Down's syndrome being dragged along the floor, and soaked with water. People with Down's syndrome can be challenging, and it requires a special type of personality to be able to absorb some of the problems and remain focused. I ought to add here that I looked after learning disability care homes as a GP, and the care provided was of the highest standard. The bad ones are now very much in the minority.

Aside from the written accounts of Down's syndrome by the people themselves and their families, the learning disabled are beginning to have a presence in the wider media, especially films. Paula Sage won a Scottish BAFTA for her role in the film *Afterlife*. Pascal Duquenne, a Belgian actor, won a Best Actor award at the Cannes Film Festival for the film *L'Huitieme Jour*. Stephen Ginnz was the first actor with Down's syndrome to play the lead in a film, *Duo*. Other actors include Chris Burke, Tommy Jessop, Edward Barbanell, Danny Aslabbagh, Rene Moreno, Pablo Panini and Jason Kingsley.

One of the most moving stories is that of the artist Judith Scott, who was one of twins, born with severe Down's syndrome and profoundly deaf. Her sister was unaffected. Judith Scott was placed in institutional care where she lived for 35 years, until the efforts of her sister and the changing medical climate effected her release. Judith Scott was an artist, primarily a sculptress who created woven fibre shapes from wool and scraps of wood. The shapes are brightly coloured but strange, and have been labelled as 'outsider art'. They are disturbing because Judith Scott is so profoundly disabled, and that affects the way we look at them. Perhaps these alien shapes are a glimpse of the true mind of someone with Down's syndrome, describing a completely different reality. Unique.

As mentioned in the previous chapters, there have been many medical and social advances for Down's syndrome in the last sixty years. This is not to say we should pat ourselves on the back and relax, because there is still a long way to go. Although we can fix a lot of the medical problems, there remains no cure for Down's syndrome, nor is there a prospect of one on the horizon. There have been some trials of a new neurotransmitter (a drug which affects brain function) which it was hoped would restore the normal workings of the brain, but these have so far proved disappointing. Down's syndrome is caused by an abnormality of gene 21, which has three arms instead of two, and some have wondered if genetic surgery is a possibility, but the workings of the genetic system are complex and still not fully understood, so that remains out of reach.

The difficulty in finding a cure for Down's syndrome has led to a number of controversial therapies being offered commercially. The main ones are:

Cell therapy

This involves the injection of dried brain cells from lamb and calf foetuses. The children are also given vitamins and thyroid extract. The proponents claim it works, while the medical establishment believes it has little or no effect. There is no theoretical reason why it should work, and an Australian study could not demonstrate any benefit. The injection of foreign material could be harmful.

Sensory integration therapy

This theory believes that learning problems are caused by difficulty processing incoming stimuli. The author, an occupational therapist called Ayers, subjected patients to a variety of stimuli, some movement-orientated, like swinging the child, or sensory, applying different objects to the skin. It had limited success, and some children did not enjoy the process.

Vitamins and minerals

It is claimed that high doses of vitamins and minerals can improve the mental and physical function of people with Down's syndrome. Formal medical trials have failed to demonstrate significant benefit. Some of the vitamins and minerals can be toxic.

Allergy diets and gluten-free diets

Some Down's syndrome children will have food allergies, just like the normal population, but there is no evidence that a blanket diet is of any value at all. Gluten sensitivity is a feature of coeliac disease, not associated with Down's syndrome, and needs a formal diagnosis by hospital investigation.

The Feingold diet

This diet was initially developed to treat hyperactivity, and involves excluding food with artificial colourings, plus some fruits. Anecdotally it appears to work in some children, although it is of questionable value in Down's syndrome.

Doman-Delacto method

This involves a series of exercises for the disabled child. The theory is that by constantly repeating movements of the head and body (patterning), the dysfunctional brain will reorganise along normal lines. The therapy is intensive, and parents normally recruit a team of helpers, which makes it time-consuming and expensive. Again, it is of doubtful value, and although some children are helped, very few are cured.

Developmental optometry

This theory believes that eye treatments – exercises, coloured lenses, and weak lenses – can improve learning. It may help for a child with behavioural problems, but not for people with Down's syndrome, who have abnormal brain function.

Chiropractic

Manipulation of the spine has been claimed to be helpful, and certainly works in the general population, but it has risks in Down's syndrome due to the instability of the vertebrae.

Medicines

As mentioned above, the search is on for a medicine which will improve mental function in Down's syndrome. Drugs that have been tried include methylphenidate, better known as Ritalin, which is commonly used to treat attention deficit hyperactivity disorder (ADHD). It doesn't appear to work in generalised Down's syndrome, but does help the Down's syndrome child with ADHD.

A newer drug, atomoxatine, has been tried, with some encouraging results, but it is probably too early to say how effective it will be.

Dore programme

This is an exercise programme invented by Wynford Dore, whose learning disability daughter benefited from the regime. There are a number of clinics across the UK.

Doctors are generally sceptical about the value of these therapies. However, at a practical level, the diet and exercise regimes can help the person with Down's syndrome and their families because it puts them in charge of a process they can influence, an important part of the therapeutic process. The problem is that the rise of the internet has seen the return of unscrupulous individuals offering dubious 'cures' for all sorts of illness. People with incurable problems, like Down's syndrome, are particularly susceptible to their wiles, because it is only natural, when you are given an 'incurable' diagnosis, to seek help elsewhere.

The second great challenge thrown up by the social and medical advances in the treatment of Down's syndrome is the question of pregnancy and marriage. This is a complex question in which expectations are frequently confounded, both for better and for worse.

There are two main factors concerning marriage, the first being the degree of disability, and the second being the condition of the partner. There are plenty of instances of people mildly affected with Down's syndrome who have married either similar people with Down's syndrome, or normally abled people, and these marriages are fine (or, at least, as fine as any marriage can be).

The difficulties increase when both people have moderate or severe disability, when you venture into the murky world of informed consent, and the degree of understanding both partners have of the nature of their union. If both partners require some form of institutional care, and will do so for the rest of their lives, where does marriage fit in that scenario? It is a very difficult question.

This is compounded tenfold by the problems of pregnancy. Theoretically, a woman with Down's syndrome has a 10 per cent chance of producing a Down's syndrome child, if the father is normally abled. The problem is, in the few cases that have been reported, the incidence seems much higher. This poses problems for counselling, and for social care, as well as an ethical dilemma. However mild the degree of Down's syndrome in the mother, she still has some degree of disability, and may therefore struggle to cope with the needs of an infant.

What of men with Down's syndrome? Very little is known, as male fertility seems to be significantly reduced, and there are few instances of fathers with Down's syndrome. Theoretically, again, the chances of their child having Down's syndrome is about 10% per cent

People with Down's syndrome should therefore have the right to enjoy loving relationships, as long as the marriage is for the right reasons and not based on a sense of duty or dependency. Having children, though, is more problematical, and needs to be thought through with a realistic assessment of the parents' capabilities. The scenario which needs to be avoided, for everybody's sake, is where both parents have learning difficulties and produce a child who is severely disabled. That is a disastrous situation for all concerned, not least the child. Sometimes the child copes with the disability better than the parents, and I have heard of situations where the parents communicated to the outside world through the child. Can you imagine that? If society has a responsibility for anything, it is surely to step into situations like these.

In telling the story of Down's syndrome, I have tried to emphasise some of the positive social changes in the care of people with Down's syndrome. The truth is, however, that there have been very few social changes in the story of Down's syndrome. I became aware when researching the story of Down's syndrome that, with a few notable exceptions, the lot of the person with learning disability, and disability in general, has been a tale of exclusion, neglect and abuse. Although the range of services and quality of education has been transformed, and the people providing the services have radically changed the perception of learning disability, the public remain unmoved. While most other minority groups have gained a wide degree of acceptance, the disabled remain outsiders.

The journalist Katherine Quarmby has detailed this in her book *Scapegoat: Why We Are Failing Disabled People.* The book covers the historical treatment of the disabled, and brings us up to date with a thorough exploration of the recent history of the disability movement. One has to say that it is a distressing read.

One of the chapters deals with the institutions which looked after disabled and learning disability children after the war. It seems that abuse and neglect in these institutions was the norm rather than exception, and it took scandals at four hospitals – Ely, Farleigh, South Ockendon, and Normansfield (of Langdon Down fame) – to expose the criminal abuse of the nation's mentally ill and disabled. Staff in many of the hospitals had 'favourites', leaving others to be victimised, which meant physical punishment. Abuse, both physical and mental, was rife, and it appears that care homes attracted people who clearly enjoyed inflicting this torture.

And worse happened. One girl in a Norfolk institution, Ann Macfarlane, saw the nurses drown another girl at bath time, holding her under the water until she died. The girl was never referred to again. This was only fifty years ago, and outside these institutions the staff responsible were probably regarded as upstanding members of the community. As the author puts it, institutions for the disabled and mentally ill seemed to operate outside of criminal law.

There is a long history of violence towards disabled people in this country, going right back to the Middle Ages and the ducking stool. *Scapegoat* details some of the most recent cases, from the imprisonment and death of Kevin Davis (which took place in a village three miles from where I live, and where I had once been a GP), to the deaths of Fiona Pilkington, Christine Lakinski, Brent Martin, and all the other disabled people humiliated and killed. What Katherine Quarmby found quite shocking was not just the level of violence directed at the disabled, but the way old tortures involving water were used, as if the modern perpetrators were somehow echoing their ancestors' rituals. Of course, most of us would regard the perpetrators as animals, not proper human beings like the rest of us. While a certain amount of this could be true, consider the following findings from *Scapegoat*:

- 90 per cent of us have never invited a disabled person into their home.
- only 20 per cent of disabled people have non-disabled friends.

How would most of us fare on these counts? I cannot remember ever inviting a disabled person into my house. I do have disabled friends, but both were the result of rugby injuries, and we were friends when they were normally abled. I have never befriended a disabled person, although in fairness I would say that as a village GP it was difficult to befriend patients. But, like anyone, I am guilty of patronising learning disability patients when I see them, and looking around for any excuse to leave after five minutes.

More worrying still is the level of violence experienced by disabled people. The author found that the majority of learning disability children were bullied at school, and that nearly half of disabled people had 'recently' witnessed or experienced physical abuse. There had also been a huge rise in disability hate crime.

I'm afraid this does not say much for our society, which is all the more galling because society has shown that it can change. The attitude of ordinary people towards racism, gay rights and women's rights has changed markedly in the past fifty years. The Britain I grew up in was overwhelmingly racist, homophobic and misogynist, attitudes which have changed dramatically, certainly as far as my children's generation are concerned. To put this in context, my father's generation would have regarded someone from another race as alien (and inferior), thought that 'poofs' should be locked up, and that women were meant to stay at home and look after the children. My children are more or less colour blind, have no problem with regarding women as equals, and would draw their friends from people of all sexual orientations. Of course it is not perfect, but attitudes are a lot better than they were fifty years ago, something which demonstrates that political correctness and affirmative action do have a positive effect. But for the disabled, and people with Down's syndrome, hardly anything has changed. They are still outsiders, mocked, feared, and ignored.

The slow pace of change has led to the radicalisation of the disabled. In 1972, a wheelchair user called Paul Hunt and a disabled South African doctor, Vic Finkelstein, set up the Union of Physically Impaired Against Segregation (UPIAS), which campaigned against the incarceration of those with physical impairment. UPIAS became a powerful advocate for the disabled, and evolved into the British Council for Disabled People.

People with Down's syndrome, however, and other learning disability people, were still the Cinderellas of the mental health and disability movements. In 1984, a young Briton with learning disability, Gary Bourlet, set up British People First, to help his fellow disabled get 'homes, real jobs, and real wages'. The nascent radical disabled fringe was finding a voice of its own, which increasingly clashed with the established charities and medical profession. The medical model of disability, which saw each disabled person as an individual medical problem to be solved, was challenged by the activists' 'social model', which believed that 'disabled people have their own identity as people with impairments in society ... the disability becomes the problem of society, not the individual disabled person'. In other words, it is the duty of society to find ways of including the disabled in society. This meant finding proper homes and jobs, and getting the support needed to function in the community. Despite the profusion of laws and initiatives aiming to improve the lot of the disabled, there were and are real problems in providing the practical support that is essential for disabled people to function in the community. Social services are almost always overstretched, as are primary care services and community mental health teams. Very often the only available housing is in the poor and run-down areas of towns and cities. And jobs are almost impossible to come by. But the pressure has resulted in change. In 2000 the Disability Rights Commission was formed, and by 2005 the Disability Discrimination Act was passed, which made it an offence to discriminate against disabled people. Change is happening for the disabled, it's just taking an awfully long time.

We must not forget people with Down's syndrome in countries less fortunate than our own, which include most of the countries of the world. It is a disturbing fact that the Western world, with 20 per cent of the world's population, consumes 80 per cent of the world's medicines. While our elderly are staggering on under the weight of thousands of pounds worth of medication – statins, heart drugs, inhalers, and the like – many of the world's poor are going without basic medicines such as antibiotics and vaccines. And a child with Down's syndrome born in a poor country won't have the access to surgery, drugs, and education that children in the West enjoy. Although I think that many people are vaguely aware of this, I am not sure that we, as a society, realise the full extent of the problem. This is one area where we, as individuals, can make a difference.

The other area where we could make a difference is in the thorny subject of human rights. No country in the world can escape blame for human rights abuses, and that includes all of us in the West. Britain has been involved in extraordinary rendition, and within our country there are minorities, including the disabled, who are persecuted, although not as viciously as occurs elsewhere. Some of the worst abuses of human rights have occurred in the countries now going through the Arab Spring, with Libya, Egypt and Syria in particular singled out as oppressive authoritarian regimes. Amnesty International selects Columbia, the Democratic Republic of the Congo, India, Israel and Turkey as countries where major abuses of human rights are occurring. I once worked with a Kurd whose home was on the Turkey/Iraq border, and he told me flatly, 'If I go home, they kill me' (that was in the days of Saddam Hussein). In the Far East, Burma and Malaysia practice overt discrimination, but all the counties in the region, including China, have a patchy record on human rights. Closer to home, the collapse of communism saw the Romanian orphanage scandal exposed, with learning disability and disabled children left in squalor in state-run nurseries. And it is rumoured that al-Qaeda used two people with Down's syndrome as suicide bombers. And although the United Nations has charters on human rights and the rights of the disabled, enforcing them has proved to be another matter altogether. We may have come far, but there's a long way to go.

Nowhere is this more apparent than in the world of work. People with learning disabilities want to work, the problem is finding a suitable job. There are not enough jobs to go round as it is, let alone jobs which cater for people who have moderate disabilities, and who may need supervision, rest periods, and so on. The organisation Remploy has a proven track record in this area, and has 45 branches throughout the country, but it cannot cover every part of England. And, of course, there is no 'one size fits all' for people with Down's syndrome, so employment has to be individually tailored. It is not an easy problem, but we could do a lot better.

The biggest advance for people with Down's syndrome, though, would be for society to accept them as they are – disabled, yes, but individual personalities just as interesting and complex as the rest of us. That will mean inviting them into mainstream society, not shutting them away, or patronising them, but treating them as friends. That is a big thing to ask, for many of us struggle to accept some normally abled people, let alone those who cannot articulate, or whose appearance we may find challenging. And of course, we all give up immediately as soon as someone with Down's syndrome displays any emotion other than fawning gratitude for our intermittent attention.

But we have to try. The treatment of those with learning disability over the millennia has been a stain on human society, confirmed by our eagerness to hide the disabled away at every opportunity. We have had nearly eight thousand years of human civilisation, with our own society taking shape over the last three thousand. It would be nice to think that in the twenty-first century we could finally welcome people with Down's syndrome into all aspects of that society.

It is not going to be easy, because we find it hard to accept people trapped in bodies which we may find repulsive. And we are not going to do it alone; we are going to need political initiatives, not just in our country but globally. But even then political action can only take us so far. It will take a change in all of us, a fundamental change which allows us to see a person with Down's syndrome as a friend, not a freak. In other words, to adapt the second of the two great Commandments, 'to treat your Down's syndrome neighbour as you would treat yourself'. Put like that, how can we refuse the challenge?

Bibliography

Karen Armstrong, *Islam*, Phoenix, 2000.
The celebrated religious writer's account of Islam.

Sebastian Brandt, *A Ship of Fools*, Folio Society, 1971.
First published in 1494, Brandt's *Narrenshiff*, or ship of fools, had something to say on virtually all aspects of fifteenth-century society, depicting a world overrun with fools.

Alan Ereira and Terry Jones, *Terry Jones' Medieval Lives*, BBC Books, 2005.
A guide to the social life of the Middle Ages told through the lives of individuals – Outlaw, Monk, Damsel, etc. They create a picture of mediaeval life which is considerably more civilised than we had supposed.

Robert Fossier, *The Axe and the Oath*, Cochrane, 2010.
A more scholarly interpretation of mediaeval life.

Michel Foucault, *Madness and Civilisation*, Random House, 1965.
Foucault's complex account of society's relationship to the mentally ill.

Sir Francis Galton, *Hereditary Genius*, Classic Reprint, Forgotten Books, 2009.
The quotations in Chapter 4, pp. 60–1, are taken from this work.

Hippocrates, *Hippocrates, vols I and II*, trans. W. H. S. Jones, Heinemann, 1923.
A translation from the Greek of Hippocrates' works, quoted in Chapter 3.

Nigel Hunt, *The World of Nigel Hunt: The Diary of a Mongoloid*, Darwin Findlayson, 1967.
A groundbreaking publication, the first book published by someone with Down's syndrome. An account of the book opens Chapter 7.

Ian Kershaw, *Hitler 1936–1945: Nemesis,* Allen Lane, 2001.
The source for the story of Nazi Germany in Chapter 4.

R. D. Laing, *The Divided Self,* Tavistock Publications, 1960 (Penguin, new edn, 1990).
Laing's challenge to conventional psychiatry, of tangential interest in Down's syndrome, but essential reading for anyone who wishes to understand the modern approach to psychiatry.

John McManners (ed.), *The Oxford Illustrated History of Christianity,* Oxford University Press, 1990.

Ladelle McWhorter, *Racism and Sexual Oppression in Anglo-America,* Indiana University Press, 2009.
The mission statement of the Eugenics Record Office comes from this work.

Roy Porter (ed.), *The Cambridge Illustrated History of Medicine,* Cambridge University Press, 1996.
A comprehensive, well-illustrated, single-volume history of medicine, which takes the reader from prehistory to the present day. I relied on it for much of the history in Chapter 3, in particular the Greek and Roman periods.

Roy Porter, *Madness: A Brief History,* Oxford University Press, 2002.
A short gallop through the history of madness, this is a very useful primer for those who wish an overview of the subject.

Katherine Quarmby, *Scapegoat: Why We Are Failing Disabled People,* Portobello, 2011.
A harrowing exploration of how badly ordinary people and the authorities treat disabled people (see Chapter 7). Anyone who is interested in the disabled should read this book.

J. M. Roberts, *The Pelican History of the World,* Pelican, 1980.

Mark Selikowitz *Down Syndrome: The Facts,* Oxford University Press, 1990.
Dr Selikowitz is a Consultant Developmental Paediatrician in Sydney, Australia. This is a concise, well-written account of Down's syndrome, ranging through the medical, behavioural and educational aspects of the condition. I used it as the source for nearly all the technical aspects of Down's syndrome. The list of educational options in Chapter 5 and the controversial therapies in Chapter 7 are taken from this book.

Edward Shorter, *A History of Psychiatry*, John Wiley, 1997.
This is an essential book for anyone looking for a comprehensive history of psychiatry. I used it as the principal source for the historical psychiatric content of Chapters 1–4. Most of the quotations in those chapters are from this book.

Kathryn Lynard Soper (ed.), *Gifts*, Seagullah, 2007.
A series of reflections by mothers of Down's syndrome children, quoted in Chapter 7.

David Wright and Anne Digby (eds), *From Idiocy to Mental Deficiency*, Routledge, 1996.
This is a collection of academic essays on the social history of learning disability. It was particularly useful for understanding the distinction between 'lunatics' and 'idiots', and the evolution of care for learning disabilities from mediaeval times to the present day. The content of pp. 24–5, 49 and 55 relies on this work.

Websites

www.downs-syndrome.org.uk (Down's Syndrome Association)
www.dsrf-uk.org (The Down Syndrome Research Foundation UK))
www.downsyndromeresearch.org (The Down Syndrome Research Online Advocacy Group)
www.nhs.uk/conditions/Downs-syndrome
www.dhg.org.uk (Down's Heart Group)
www.dseinternational.org (Down Syndrome Education International)
www.downsyndrometraining.co.uk (The Down Syndrome Training and Support Service)
www.education.gov.uk (web address for Down's syndrome quite complex, use search box)
www.direct.gov.uk (link for social services)
www.bbc.co.uk (again, the address is complex, use search box)
www.camphill.org.uk (Camphill)
www.mind.org.uk (Mind)
www.mencap.org.uk (Mencap)
www.ndss.org (National Down Syndrome Society)
www.nads.org (National Association for Down Syndrome)
These last two are the main Down 's syndrome charities in the USA.
The following are web articles I used in research:
Dominic Lawson, www.independent.co.uk/opinion/commentators/ dominic-lawson.
Simon Barnes, www.women.timesonline.co.uk/tol/life_and_style/ women/families.

Some of the information on the ancient world I found in an article by Victoria Brignell in the *New Statesman*, www.newstatesman.org.

Judith Scott's work can be seen at www.judithscott.org.

Helen Zueger's story, by her mother, Angela Zueger-Caplan is at http://helenthelightourlight.blogspot.com.

Index

Action T4 72–74
AFP (alpha-fetoprotein) 87
Age of Enlightenment 3
Albert, Prince 12
Alzheimer's disease, relation to Down's syndrome 107–109
American Breeders Association 62
American Psychiatric Association 29, 31
amniocentesis 87
anaesthesia 85
antidepressants 86
Arab Spring 131
Aristotle 37
Aryan race 70–71
Asperger's syndrome 99
Astley, Lord 12

barbiturates 68
Barnes, Simon 121
Battie, William 18
Bedlam 17, 21
Beveridge, William 79
Bicêtre Hospital, Paris 24
Bodmin, St Lawrence's Hospital 79
Bourlet, Gary 130
Bowes-Lyon sisters 14, 50
Bouhler and Brandt 72
Brandt, Sebastian 50
Bremer, Ann 120
British People First 130
Broad Street water pump 3
Brookwood Hospital 29

California 62
Camphill Trust, 93
Care in the Community 14
Cardiazol 69

Cathars 51
Catholic Church 49, 51
cell therapy 124
Cerletti, Ugo 69
Chiarugi, Vincenzio 18
chiropractic 125
chorio-villus sampling 87
Christianity 43–44
Church of England 54
Colney Hatch 23
coma therapy 68
communication passport 102
Community Learning Disability Teams (CLDT) 106–110
Compendium der Psychiatrie 31
Connelly, John 12
County Lunatic Asylum Act 24
County Asylums, establishment of 24
'curables' 22
Curie, Marie 3, 70

Darwin, Charles 3, 70
Davis, Kevin 128
day hospitals 81
degeneracy 6, 27–28
de Grobineau, Arthur 70
depression 87
developmental optometry 125
diets 124
Disability Discrimination Act 131
Disability Living Allowance 80
Disability Rights Commission 131
Doman-Docatto method 125
Dore Program 126
Down, John Haydon Langdon 1–15, 28, 58, 97, 130, 146
    - attitude to women, 6

- Earlswood 6
- Normansfield 14
- 'Observations on the ethnic classification of Idiots' 5
- religious faith 6
Down's syndrome
- alternative treatments 125–126
- education 88–91, 97–104
- features 9–10
- medical treatments for 85–88
- mosaic variant 121
- physical characteristics 10
Down's Syndrome Association 104
Down Syndrome Educational Trust 108
Down's Heart Group 108
Down's Syndrome Research Foundation 108
Duffy, John 67
Duquenne, Pascal 123

Earlswood Hospital 4, 13–14, 24, 27
electroconvulsive therapy, ECT 69
Education Act 1981 92
Egypt, Ancient 36
eugenics 60–64
eugenics programme USA 62

Faraday, Michael 2
Feingold diet 125
fever cure 68
Finkelstein, Victor 130
Foucault, Michael 51, 82
Fool, the 50
Freud, Sigmund 4

Galen 40–41
Galton, Sir Francis 60–61
genocide 59, 72, 74
German psychiatry 19–21
Gifts 118, 122, 136

Ginnz, Stephen 123
Goffman, Ervine 96
Great Terror, Russian 74
Greece, Ancient 37–39

Heart of the Forest School 100–105
Henry VIII 54
Hitler, Adolf 69–74
Himroth 19
Hippocrates 38–39
homosexuality 29
human rights abuses 131
humoral Theory 41
Hunt, Nigel 25, 113–118
Hunt, Paul 130

idiot 4–9, 22–25, 49–51, 55, 57, 67
- definition 49
idiocy
- causes of 22
Immigration Restriction League 62
'incurables' 22,
Inquisition 51
insulin coma therapy 68
internet 126
Islam 41–42
Itard, Jean 24

Jacobi, Dr Maximilian 19–21
Jay, John 12
Judaism 41

Kesey, Ken 83
Koch, Robert 3
Kosminski, Aaron 67
Kraft-Ebbing, Richard 29
Kraepelin, Emil 31

Laing, R. D. 82
Lakinski, Christine 128
Landsteiner, Karl 4
largactil 80

Lawson, Dominic 121
learning difficulty, definition 10
Lejeune, Jerome 86
leprosy 45
Lister, Joseph 3
Lloyd George, David 79
London Hospital 2–3
lunatics 4, 27, 54

Macfarlane, Ann 128
Magnan, Valentin 28
Malleus Maleficarum 53
Makaton 102
Martin, Brent 128
Meduna, Ladislas von 68
Mendel, Gregor 3
Milledgeville Asylum 66
MIND 80
Miramar, Maria Teresa Ferrari de 67
mongolism 6–9
Morel, Benedict 27–28
Morton, William 3
Muhammed 42

National Health Service 79
Negro Project Conspiracy Theory 65
New Labour 93
Norman society 48–49

'Observations on an ethnic classification for Idiots' 5
Olmecs 34–36
One Flew Over The Cuckoo's Nest 16, 83
Ordinalia 50
outlaws 53

P scales 103
Palmerston, Lord 12
Pasteur, Louis 3
Peliman, Karl 30

pharmacology 85
Pilkington, Fiona 128
Pinel, Phillipe 18
Plato 37
Plumbe, Anne Serena 12
Powell, Enoch 78
Primary Care Trusts 111
The Protocols of the Elders of Zion 70
psychiatry
  - early 19–23
  - aims of twentieth century 80
Pullen, John 13

Quarmby, Katherine 128

Razi, Muhammed ibn Zakariya 42
Reed, Revd Andrew 12
Reformation 54–56
Reil, Johan 18
Remploy 132
Rome, Ancient 39–40
Romulus 39
Rontgen 3
Rothschild, Baron 12
Royal Commission on the law relating to mental illness and mental deficiency 1957, 81
Rush, Benjamin 18

Sage, Paula 123
scrofula 45
Scapegoat 128
Scott, Judith 123
Seigburg 22
sensory integration therapy 124
Seneb 37
Ship of Fools 50
Signalong 103
Snow, John 3
Sonnenstein 22
Stalin 74
Statement of Educational Needs 97

Steiner, Rudolph 93
syphilis 68
Szasz, Thomas 83

termination of pregnancy 88
Tiergartenstrabe 4, 72
Trisomy 21 86
Tuke, William 18

Ubermenschen 70
Union of Physically Impaired
    against Segregation 130

Victoria, Queen 12
Victorian philanthropy 12
vitamins 124
Von Meduna, Ladislav 80

Wagner-Juaregg, Julius 68
Water Tower Speech 78
witchcraft 53
World Health Organisation 20